Surface Mount Technology

Surface Mount Technology

Recent Japanese Developments

Preeminent articles from the journal
Surface Mount Technology, published in Japanese by
Press Journal Inc.

Translated by TechSearch International, Inc.

Edited by Jan Vardaman

 IEEE
PRESS

Published in cooperation with the IEEE Components, Hybrids,
and Manufacturing Technology Society

The Institute of Electrical and Electronics Engineers, Inc., New York

This book may be purchased at a discount from the publisher
when ordered in bulk quantities. For more information contact:

IEEE PRESS Marketing
Attn: Special Sales
P.O. Box 1331
445 Hoes Lane
Piscataway, NJ 08855-1331
Fax: (908) 981-8062

Printed in the United States of America

10 9 8 7 6 5 4 3 2 1

ISBN 0-7803-0407-1

IEEE Order Number: PC0302-0

Library of Congress Cataloging-in-Publication Data

Surface mount technology : recent Japanese developments / translated
by TechSearch International, Inc.
    p.   cm.
    "Preeminent articles from the journal Surface mount technology,
published in Japanese by Press Journal, Inc."
    "Published in cooperation with the IEEE Components, Hybrids, and
Manufacturing Technology Society."
    "IEEE order number : PC0302-0"—T.P. verso.
    Includes bibliographical references and index.
    ISBN 0-7803-0407-1
    1. Printed circuits—Design and construction. 2. Surface mount
technology. 3. Printed circuit industry—Japan. I. TechSearch
International. II. IEEE Components, Hybrids, and Manufacturing
Technology Society. III. Hyomen jisso gijutsu.
TK7868.P7S87   1993   92-53186
                                                   CIP

Contents

Foreword

Just as the motto of the Olympic Games is *citius, altius, fortius* (translated as faster, higher, stronger), so electronics packaging is ever pushing the limits to provide more function, more value, higher reliability in the designs and products from our companies. The move to surface-mount components significantly increases density, allowing a high degree of functionality in a handheld radio or cellular phone, in the controller for a miniaturized disk drive, in the full-featured laptop computer, or in the flat-panel display.

Is this a revolution in packaging? Perhaps not, in many senses, but SMT requires relearning and retooling. In the 1950s and 1960s, electronics moved away from hand-soldered wires wrapped around terminal strips, to embrace a new technology—wave soldering. I spent several years as a manufacturing engineer refining that process: experimenting with automatic insertion, inclined conveyors, different nozzles, various fluxes and speeds. Always there was the challenge of process control—cleanliness, preheat, dwell, cooldown, and touch-up. We are now undergoing a similar conversion as surface mount becomes the method of choice for many applications.

The change to SMT makes us relearn, starting with the basics, exactly how to run an electronics assembly operation. We depend to a great extent on the infrastructure that supplies the equipment, materials, and components for this process. Yet, it is never as simple as purchasing the "right" equipment and turning it on. There are design issues that affect assembly, and a considerable number of variables that can affect the quality and yield through the process. Components have new and unique failure modes and handling requirements. That's where the discerning engineer must not only learn about the particular process being implemented within his/her company, but must also be aware of developments and trends that can favorably impact the process. It is in the spirit of inquiring into state-of-the-art improvements that the Institute of Electrical and Electronics Engineers (IEEE), Inc. has prepared this book and worked to bring it to you.

Challenges in the electronics industry require the efforts of more than just one company or one country—they require the communication of ideas and experiences across major boundaries. Substantial advances in SMT have taken place in Japan, and until now, most of the major publications reporting these results have been available only to those who could read Japanese. Engineers in other major markets could see the resulting products, but did not have ready access to the experiments and analysis underlying them.

Press Journal, Inc., recognizing the importance of global understanding in the electronics industry, agreed to allow the IEEE to publish selected articles from its special issues on surface mount technology. IEEE's Components, Hybrids, and Manufacturing Technology (CHMT) Society has been effective in bringing the international community together to achieve communication of ideas and problem-solving across the international community.

I am indebted to the hard work of Jan Vardaman of TechSearch International for agreeing to be the editor for this undertaking. She is well connected with the technologists writing the original papers, and the work of their companies, and her contacts within Japan are numerous. The considerable challenge was the complete translation of the articles, which appeared only in Japanese, to make them available to the broader technical community. It is my hope that further sharing of the technology undergirding SMT will be possible in the future, and additional developments from around the world—and especially from Japan—will become available through vehicles such as this volume.

Paul Wesling
Advisory Design Engineer, Tandem Computers, Inc.
Vice-President, Publications
CHMT Society of the IEEE

Preface

Surface mount technology (SMT) has developed rapidly over the past ten years. Today, 90 percent of the components in a personal computer or laptop are surface mounted. Advances continue to be made in SMT, but challenges such as fine pitch bonding and equipment development remain.

Challenges in the electronics industry require the efforts of more than just one company or one country. They require the communication of ideas and experiences across major boundaries. Major advancements in SMT have taken place in Japan, and until now most of the major publications have been available only to those who could read Japanese.

Press Journal, Inc., recognizing the importance of global understanding in the electronics industry, agreed to allow the IEEE to publish selected articles from its special issues on SMT. The IEEE Components, Hybrids, and Manufacturing Technology Society has been effective in bringing the international community together to achieve communication of ideas and problem-solving across the international community.

TechSearch International, Inc. is proud to assist in bringing these parties together and translating these important SMT articles. Topics appearing in this publication include new surface mount packages such as molded plastic packages, tape automated bonding, and flip-chip bonded packages. Also included are reliability data on these packages, as well as mounting equipment developed in Japan.

This book would not have been possible without the sponsorship of the IEEE CHMT Society, the assistance of CHMT Publications Vice President, Paul Wesling, and the long hours of translation by Kazumi Allen, Dan Garrett, James Parker, Michael S. Turner, and Fujiko Takai Signs. Technical review by Dr. Avram Bar-Cohen of the University of Minnesota, Mary Wesling Hartnett of TechSearch International, Mike McShane of Motorola, Oscar Vaz of Apple Computer, and Paul Wesling of Tandem Computers provided great assistance by improving the accuracy of the translations and helping to guide the editing process. Guidance by Eugene J. Rymaszewski, Associate Director of the Center for Integrated Electronics at Rensselaer Polytechnic Institute and Executive Advisor to TechSearch

International, has been essential throughout the project, and the comments provided by John Lau of Hewlett-Packard aided in the early stages of the project.

The IEEE PRESS, through Executive Director Dudley Kay, Production Supervisor Denise Gannon, and Associate Editor Anne Reifsnyder, has brought all the pieces together and financed the necessary translations, permissions, and production costs. The enthusiasm of the PRESS editors and their suggestions for improving upon the original plan are gratefully acknowledged and appreciated.

Jan Vardaman

Part 1

Trends
in Surface Mount
Technology

Interconnect Technology in the 1990s

Kaszumichi Machida

Mitsubishi Electric Corp.

INTRODUCTION

In electronic products such as information and communications equipment, competition extends beyond the development of customized large-scale integration (LSI) and into the development of attractive end products. As products become increasingly lighter, smaller, and capable of advanced functions, consumer demand needs to be stimulated by a smorgasbord of products having a short life cycle as well as low cost. Advances will naturally be demanded of mounting substrates, which are a key component of these products, but it is difficult to predict the most significant developments in interconnect technology in the 1990s. In this article we will look at the constituent technologies and advances in bonding technologies for the emerging interconnect technologies.

TECHNOLOGICAL TRENDS

Several types of interconnect methods for electronic products are shown in Fig. 1. Figure 2 shows the predicted trend for each type. The vertical axis is the mounting density (the number of bonds per unit surface area of the substrate), which is an indicator of technological progress.

In 1992, present surface mount technology (SMT) will be almost fully mature as it replaces the long-standing through-hole method. The widespread adoption of SMT has in turn brought down the cost of surface mount components. Furthermore, tape automated bonding (TAB) components and general-pur-

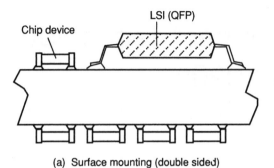

(a) Surface mounting (double sided)

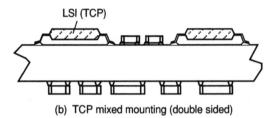

(b) TCP mixed mounting (double sided)

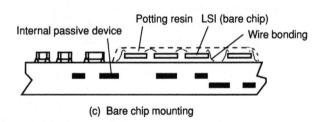

(c) Bare chip mounting

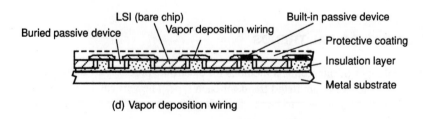

(d) Vapor deposition wiring

Fig. 1   Various mounting methods.

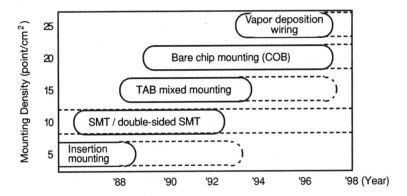

Fig. 2 Progress in mounting. The solid line shows development period, the dashed line application period.

pose components will be mixed together to increase the mounting density of leading-edge end products. Beyond this, we can expect the emergence of chip on board (COB) applications wherein a bare chip is die bonded so that the chip electrodes are connected directly to the substrate pattern. Mounting efficiency will be improved by arranging and interconnecting several bare chips closely together in a multichip module configuration.

In the second half of the 1990s, the following technologies will be realized: 1) consolidation of the substrate and chassis to decrease the size of end products; 2) three-dimensional mounting, in which passive device functions are built into the substrate's inner layers so that more LSI chips can be mounted on the surface; 3) the imbedding of bare chips in the insulation material of the substrate and deposition wiring using a focused ion beam with a metal ion source; and 4) deposition wiring with implanted functional components. What follows is a summary of predictions on the direction of major constituent technologies that will bring about these developments.

Interconnect Design: CAD → Design for Reliability Performance

The design process presently begins with product design, followed by other design decisions such as the arrangement of components. Within this process, factors such as the yield of the soldering process are considered.

In the future, as minute interconnections are packed more closely together, it becomes necessary to have a design philosophy that maintains the product quality demanded of each interconnection. For instance, an excessive amount of soldering will cause a large number of solder bridges in the soldering process. Thus, in substrate mounting design, an understanding of the minimum solder amount and lead pitch required to ensure long term reliability (under conditions such as heat fatigue) of the interconnections must take precedence.

Mounting Components: 0.5 mm QFP → 0.2 mm TCP, 1608 → 1005

The issue for high density is the number of components that can be put on the substrate. The starting point is to make advanced functional components as small as possible. In addition, the miniaturization of end products has created a demand for components with thin profiles.

Two years have passed since quad flat packages (QFPs) with a 0.5 mm lead pitch were first commercialized. As Fig. 3 indicates, the narrower lead pitch reduced the package footprint to one-half that of an identical package with a 0.65 mm pitch QFP and 100 pins. Furthermore, the package thickness was halved, to 1.3 mm. This package is now regarded as a mainstream general-purpose package of the future. Meanwhile, 0.3 mm-pitch special-purpose gate array packages have

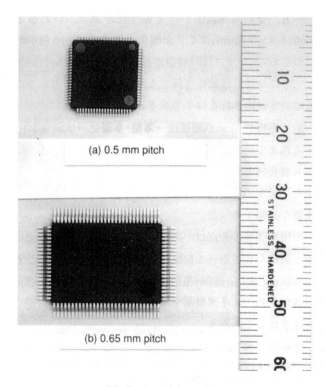

Fig. 3   A quad flat package.

been mounted on leading-edge products such as computers and electronic equipment.

Paralleling this development, TAB technology is now maturing as tape carrier packages (TCPs) reach the market. As a result, packages have been significantly reduced in size, to less than one-fourth the size of a 0.65 mm QFP. With a lead pitch less than 200 µm and lead space of approximately 100 µm, they are in a range suitable for present LSI bonding pitch.

While some industry observers think that LSIs with pin counts exceeding 500 pins will shift toward pin grid arrays, it is likely that the majority of packages in the 1990s will move ahead with QFP packages because of cost and mass production considerations.

Meanwhile, passive components have also been undergoing miniaturization, with 1005 (1.0 mm × 0.5 mm) components being the smallest commercially available at present. Chip resistors are in the mass production stage [1] and capacitors, having already completed product quality and reliability evaluation, will soon be available in stable supply.

Substrate Materials: Low TCE → Thinner
Substrate with More Layers → Lower Dielectric

Up to now, the main emphasis in improving the characteristics of composite materials has been on reducing the thermal coefficient of expansion and reducing resistance to higher operating temperatures. In the consumer equipment market, this emphasis was combined with the reduction of manufacturing costs.

The main emphasis in the future development of thinner substrates having more layers will be a shift toward high precision lamination and minute throughhole formation. Also, with the trend toward high frequency signal processing for information and communications equipment, development will accelerate in high performance substrates with an emphasis on noise reduction. Furthermore, beyond bare chip mounting, it is predicted that serious efforts will be made to develop and proliferate substrates that conform to LSIs and have high heat dissipation as well.

Interconnection: Fine Soldering → Bonding

The miniaturization of packages and chip components will inevitably lead to finer interconnection. As will be discussed later, fine interconection technology is at the core of the trend toward higher density. Because the present mainstream SMT combination of solder paste printing and batch reflow soldering is extremely high in productivity, improvements will push solder, printer, printing mask, and reflow heat source technologies to their limit in fineness. Components beyond this limit (0.2 mm lead pitch) will be accommodated with solder plating and localized reflow. Because this type of interconnect for discrete components is expected to increase in the future, development is being accelerated in making equipment and process technologies higher in efficiency and stability. Furthermore, in bare chip mounting, because the wire bonding or TAB inner lead bonding in the LSI chip assembly process is performed on the substrate, the assembly line will require a clean room level of less than class 10,000.

Mounting and Inspection Equipment: High Precision → Intelligent

For fine-featured interconnections that are high in quality and reliability, it is necessary to increase the precision for all measurement parameters relating to the interconnection. That is, in addition to managing the substrate pattern, lead formation of components, and solder supply volume, the required precision level for component placing is 10 μm, equivalent to LSI assembly equipment. Furthermore, component placers will be introduced that can perform high speed verification of lead shapes and place components in the optimal position based on a comprehensive decision. Interconnect inspection equipment will have the ability to make comparisons with advanced high-reliability design standards and make accurate decisions.

DIRECTION OF INTERCONNECT TECHNOLOGY

Figure 4 shows the flow of representative mounting processes in the future. The incorporation of TCPs will be done for the time being with a separate outer lead bonding process after the batch reflow process. However, because TCPs will soon be used in mass-produced consumer equipment, leading semiconductor suppliers have already completed the development of packages that reliably resist heat and can withstand the batch reflow process. Figure 5 is a photograph of outer lead bonds. Presently the most widely used heat source is a resistance heat source called *pulse heat*. Ensuring a stable bonding quality for lead pitches below 0.2 mm requires even heat and pressure, for which it is necessary to optimize the chip material and shape.

In the near future, a series of processes such as inner lead bonding (ILB), molding, and lead processing will be formed into a sub-line of the assembly process line. In Fig. 6, the lead pitch for TAB inner lead bonds has been narrowed using a zigzag pattern. Where the outer lead bonding (OLB) is done with soldering, the ILB uses thermocompression. This example uses TB-TAB (transferred bump tape automated bonding) in which the gold bumps are formed not on the

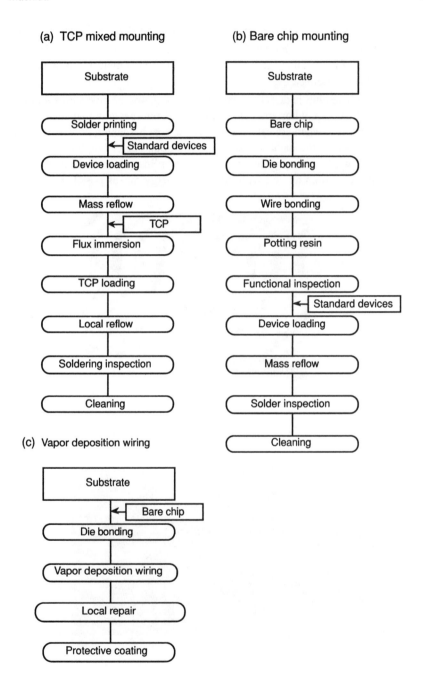

Fig. 4   Process flow for various mounting methods.

LSI electrodes but on the tape leads. Because a special bump formation process is not needed on the bare chip after the wafer process, TAB can be used freely in a wide variety of LSIs. Thus TB-TAB is expected to be the mainstream in the diffusion of TAB technology.

When a bare chip is directly mounted as in Fig. 4b, the first step should be to mount the LSI chip, whose pad cleanliness has been specially managed. In the die bonding process when adhesives are used, the heat hardening process accelerates the oxidation of the pads. Thus, a short-duration solder bonding method is preferred. The wire bonding is the same as in the ordinary LSI assembly process. Thermocompression combined with ultrasonic energy makes possible relatively

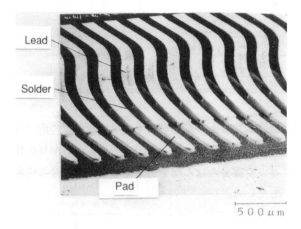

Fig. 5   Tape automated bonding outer lead bonding.

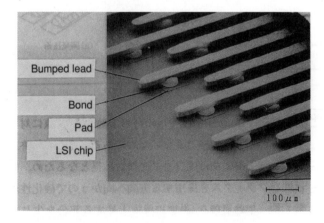

Fig. 6   Tape automated bonding inner lead bonding.

low bonding temperatures, thereby suppressing substrate oxidation and allowing for greater stability in the batch reflow process that follows. However, in using ultrasonic energy effectively on the bonds, it is critical that the substrate be firmly held in place. The limit in pin count for bare chips is imposed not by wedge bonding on the substrate but by the ball bonding on the chip electrodes. In other words, the large diameter of the end of the capillary tool causes it to touch adjacent bonds, limiting the pitch to around 90 μm [2]. However, when the multichip effect is considered, it is possible to obtain a maximal mounting efficiency with current methods. Silicone resin is actively being developed as a potting material with exceptional heat resistance and hermeticity.

There are issues remaining in batch reflow soldering on accommodating finer leads on general-purpose components. First, from the printing process to the reflow process, it will be necessary to manage higher clean levels than ever before. This is because as substrates come to have a large number of narrow pitch bonds, the effect of particles on printing precision and the fusion and flow characteristics of solder cannot be ignored. Also, as noncleaning or freonless cleaning is presumed in the final process, the trend will be toward deactivated flux. Thus a low oxidizing, even-heating reflow heat source is preferred. In other words, a furnace with an inert atmosphere such as vapor phase soldering (VPS), which ensures even heating, is best.

The problem of bridging becomes serious as the lead pitch decreases. When observed closely, the melting solder was found to be either in good condition or bridged when it reached equilibrium. However, by controlling the flow of the melting solder, bridgeless soldering can be accomplished with stability even if the solder paste has a short prior to soldering. The flow control technology we developed is described in Fig. 7. In this example, the printing pattern was modified to take advantage of the fact that as the solder on the pads starts to spread, it draws away any solder that might cause a bridge.

CONCLUSION

Spurred by the demand for small size and high performance in electronic products, the progress in high density mounting technology knows no bounds. For the time being, the technology will advance along the present lines of fixing and connecting available components onto the substrate. Beyond that, the technology will start to encroach on LSI territory.

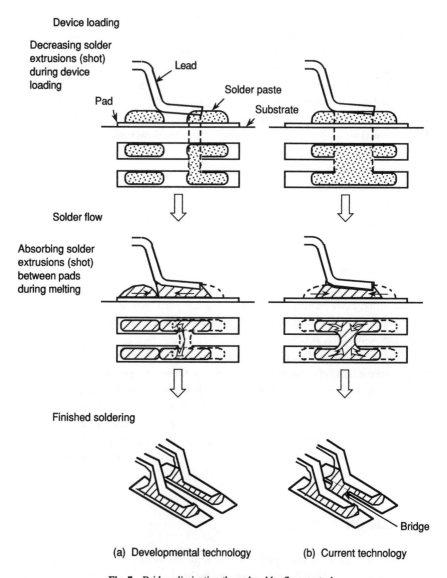

Device loading

Decreasing solder
extrusions (shot)
during device
loading

Pad

Lead

Solder paste

Substrate

Solder flow

Absorbing solder
extrusions (shot)
between pads
during melting

Finished soldering

Bridge

(a) Developmental technology   (b) Current technology

Fig. 7 Bridge elimination through solder flow control.

REFERENCES

[1] "Surface Mount Technology," special issue of *Nikkei Electronics,* no. 495, p. 119, March 19, 1990

[2] Machita, "Bonding," *Japan Metal Assn. Report,* vol. 28, no. 1, p. 70, 1989.

Standardization and Recent Trends in LSI Packages for SMT

Tooru Tachikawa
Minoru Yoshida

Mitsubishi Electric Corp.

INTRODUCTION

Equipment is becoming increasingly lightweight, thin, and compact as exemplified by VCR cameras and notebook personal computers. Surface mount technology (SMT) is being applied because it is a good method in terms of the efficient use of surface area or cubic space. Surface mount–type packages that bring out the best in large scale integration (LSI) chip performance are being developed and marketed in package series. From the point of view of standardization, the latest trends can be summarized as follows:

1. Mainstream plastic packages have achieved higher pin counts, narrower lead pitches, and smaller bodies.

2. These packages were standardized in the early stages of development by the Semiconductor Package Dimensions Committee (EE-13) of the EIAJ. A standard line-up has been established up to the super-300 pin level with SSOPs and shrink quad flat packages (QFPs).

3. For tape automated bonding (TAB) packages, which are the next generation of SMT, sufficient progress is being made for packages up to the super-500 pin class as well as for logic, memory, and other applications.

In addition to outlining standardization trends for SMT LSI packages, this paper introduces the crucial elements of the current state of package manufacturing process technology and surface mount technology.

PACKAGE TRENDS

As is well known, the three methods of achieving lighter and smaller end products through packaging techniques are SMT (surface mounting of the finished package), COB (direct mounting of the bare chip to the substrate) and FC (flip chip mounting using an intermediary bump). It is difficult to give a simple summary of the advantages and disadvantages of each of these packaging methods. However, the three main factors that can be used to constitute a standard by which to make a selection are packaging efficiency, the characteristics of the semiconductor's yield, and burn-in demands. First, as Fig. 1 shows, in terms of packaging efficiency, the SMT and COB methods are at the same appropriate level while the FC method is the most efficient [1]. However, when yield and burn-in are considered, the SMT finished package is the best.

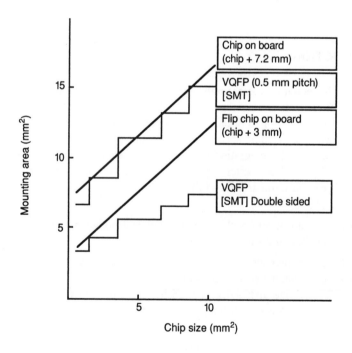

Fig. 1 Relation of chip size to mounting area.

Smaller Size, Higher Pin Count

Next we will investigate the current state and future prospects of efforts to decrease package size and increase pin count. Figure 2 gives a comparison of existing package pin counts and mounting area [2]. This figure uses examples from Mitsubishi products and there is some small variation in these figures for other manufacturers. In this figure, the movement toward the downward, right-hand direction exemplifies decreased package size and increased pin count. In addition to the issue of mounting technology, the packages with the highest pin density are, at the present time, those with a 0.5 mm lead pitch. Henceforth remarkable progress in packaging and TAB technology coupled with finer LSI chip design rules can be expected to result in an acceleration of package trends toward increased compactness and higher pin counts.

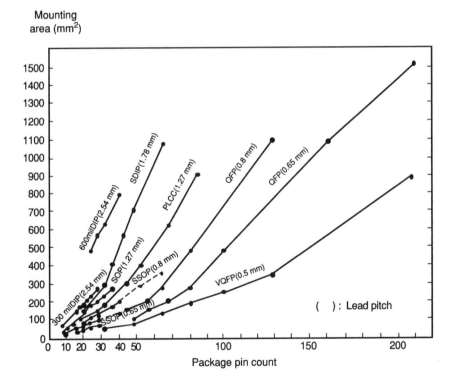

Fig. 2   Mounting area to pin count relation (the mounting area is determined from the package's maximum external dimensions).

Trends in Package Standardization

In Japan, the EIAJ's Semiconductor External Dimensions Committee (EE-13) is establishing the external dimension standards for IC packages. Within the next 1 to 2 years, standards for QFP (fine pitch), thin small outline package (TSOP), SSOP and TSOP (II) SMT packages will be offered. Also, as part of international cooperation, two joint meetings of the U.S. JEDEC (JC-11) and the EIAJ (EE-13) have resulted in joint standards for two packages, the BQFP and GQFP. In both cases the standardization adopted was for the metric method. This is a real step toward the establishment of international standards. An EE-13 working group is actively considering TCP standards. Although initially considered difficult, joint standards with JEDEC (JC-11) have become the goal through discussions at U.S.-Japanese joint meetings. In addition to these packages, EIAJ standards are expected to be adopted just as they are for TSOP, TSOP (II), and QFP (fine pitch) packages. Just as with the examples given above, standardization for new packages is proceeding on course. In January, 1990, a working group was set up to establish guidelines for standard memory products. Up to that time there hadn't been discussion about packages for specific types of products. However, as a result of the strong desire of users and JEDEC, a process of ongoing discussion is taking place to select recommended packages for specific product types. In the section above we investigated trends in package standardization. Next we will turn to an introduction of specific examples of compact, high pin count packages.

TSOP Packages. Figure 3 shows a 1-mm-thick TSOP package developed for memory card ICs. The special characteristic of this package is its design, which matches the bonding pad layout and small size of LSI chips.

TSOP (II) Packages. Figure 4 shows a TSOP (II) package developed along the same lines as those for large-capacity memory card use. The package was designed to be identical in size to SOJ packages, which gives it the merit of being able to accommodate, without change, LSIs for SOJ packages. Moreover, because the 1.27 mm, 1.0 mm lead pitch is relatively large, it is easy to mount. This facilitates both wiring on the substrate and impedance matching. When mounted on glass epoxy substrate, TSOP (II) leads emerge from the long sides of the package, as compared with the TSOP package where they emerge from the short sides, which results in decreased stress on the solder joints. The value of this stress (e), is reduced to 1/2.5. The advantages and disadvantages of both types of packages are currently being considered.

QFP (Fine Pitch) Packages. Figure 5 shows a QFP package originally designed for the purpose of achieving increased compactness in video cameras [2]. At the present, it is mostly used for high pin count gate array applications. It is available in a series that goes up to the 300 pin level.

TCP Package (TAB). Table 1 shows the transition from the wire bonding method packages used up to the present to TCP (see Fig 6). While it would

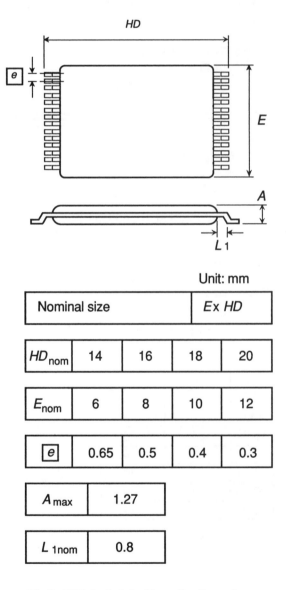

Unit: mm

Nominal size				Ex *HD*

HD_{nom}	14	16	18	20

E_{nom}	6	8	10	12

$\boxed{e}$	0.65	0.5	0.4	0.3

A_{max}	1.27

L_{1nom}	0.8

Fig. 3 EIAJ standards for thin small outline packages.

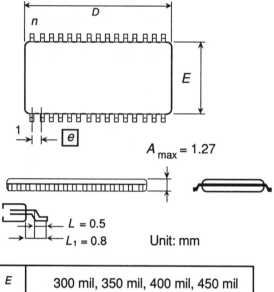

E	300 mil, 350 mil, 400 mil, 450 mil
D	475 mil to 1,025 mil (50 mil step)
e	1.0 to 1.27

D	Pin count (n)	
	e = 1.27	e = 1.0
12.06	18	24
13.33	20	26
14.6	22	28
15.87	24	30
17.14	26	34
18.41	28	36
20.95	32	40
26.03	40	—

Fig. 4   EIAJ standards for thin small outline packages (II).

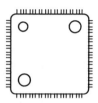

Square type

Body dimension	Maximum pin count		
	0.5 mm pitch	0.4 mm pitch	0.3 mm pitch
5 mm ^{2}	32 pins	40 pins	56 pins
7 mm ^{2}	48 pins	64 pins	80 pins
10 mm ^{2}	72 pins	88 pins	120 pins
12 mm ^{2}	88 pins	112 pins	144 pins
14 mm ^{2}	100 pins	128 pins	176 pins
20 mm ^{2}	152 pins	192 pins	256 pins
24 mm ^{2}	184 pins	232 pins	304 pins
28 mm ^{2}	216 pins	272 pins	360 pins

Rectangular type

Body dimension	Maximum pin count		
	0.5 mm pitch	0.4 mm pitch	0.3 mm pitch
5 x 7 mm	40 pins	52 pins	68 pins
7 x 10 mm	60 pins	76 pins	100 pins
10 x 14 mm	80 pins	108 pins	148 pins
14 x 20 mm	128 pins	160 pins	216 pins
20 x 28 mm	184 pins	232 pins	308 pins

Fig. 5   Fine pitch quad flat package.

appear that increasing pin counts have encouraged the change to TCP, precisely speaking it has been the increasingly finer levels of LSI design rule and the accompanying decrease in bonding pad pitch that has served as the major impetus in the shift to TAB. Because at the same time there has been progress toward increased compactness and higher pin counts, as exemplified by gate arrays, the perception has arisen that TAB technology equals high pin counts. Thirty-five-millimeter tape is available in super formats, while 48-mm and 70-mm tape is available in super and wide formats. Package maximum pin count determines package body size and the number of test pads on the tape. Seventy-millimeter tape is adaptable to a maximum of 544 pins. Figures 7 and 8 show a very thin TCP package that is less than 1.0 mm thick and is compatible with both memory IC use TSOP and TSOP (II) packages. These packages are under continuous examination by the EIAJ and it is possible that the dimensions of some parts will change.

TABLE 1   Pin Counts and Package Body Sizes for QFP, QFP (Fine Pitch), and TCP

Pin count	Package body size			
	0.8 mm pitch QFP	0.65 mm pitch QFP	0.5 mm fine pitch QFP	0.25 mm pitch TAB
80	14 × 20 mm			
100		14 × 20 mm	14 mm^2	
120	28 mm^2			
128	28 mm^2		14 × 20 mm	
136		28 mm^2		
160		28 mm^2		
208		36 mm^2	28 mm^{2*}	
256			36 mm^{2*}	
288				20 mm^{2*}
304			40 mm^{2*}	
320				24 mm^{2*}
432				32 mm^{2*}
480				36 mm^{2*}
544				40 mm^{2*}

*Under development

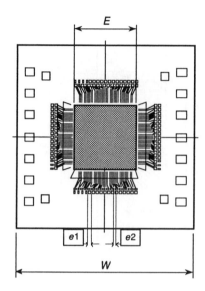

Lead pitch: 0.5, 0.4, 0.3, 0.2, 0.15
Test pad pitch: 0.25, 0.3

(Unit: mm)

Lead pitch : [e1]		0.25		Tape width (w)	Device dimension (E)
Test pad pitch : [e2]		0.5	0.4		
Device dimension (E)	14 mm²	192 pins	192 pins	35 Super	← 20 mm²
	16 mm²	—	224 pins		
	18 mm²		240 pins		
	20 mm²	256 pins	288 pins	48 Superwide	← 16 mm²
	24 mm²	—	320 pins		← 28 mm²
	28 mm²	416 pins	416 pins	70 Superwide	
	32 mm²	432 pins	480 pins		
	36 mm²	—	544 pins		← 24 mm²
	40 mm²	—	—		

Fig. 6 EIAJ proposal for high-pin-count TCP.

PACKAGE MANUFACTURING PROCESS AND SURFACE MOUNT TECHNOLOGY

Leading edge, high-pin-count, compact packages face a major hurdle in terms of both package manufacturing technology and mounting technology. For example,

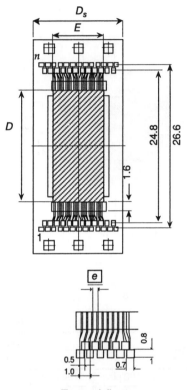

Test pad diagram

(Unit: mm)

Type	35 mm super
E	6, 8, 10, 12
D	12.4, 14.4, 16.4, 18.4
$\boxed{e}$	0.5, 0.4, 0.3
D_s	3 Perforation & 4 Perforation (E = 6, 8, 10) (E = 12)
n	48 (E = 6, 8, 10) & 68 (E = 12)

Fig. 7 Proposed EIAJ specifications for memory tape carrier package (thin small outline package).

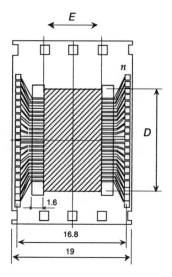

(Unit: mm)

Type	35 mm super
E	300 mil, 350 mil, 400 mil, 450 mil
D	475 mil to 1,025 mil (50 mil step)
$\boxed{e}$	1.27 & 1.0
n	40

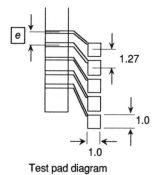

Test pad diagram

Fig. 8 Memory TCP (TSOP (II)) EIAJ specification table.

although EIAJ standards for fine pitch QFP packages exist up to the 0.3 mm pitch super-300 pin class, actual package manufacturing and mounting technologies are capable of being applied only to the 0.5 mm pitch level.

Stress

In order to decrease LSI chip stress caused by differences in the coefficient of thermal expansion with the mold resin, the Young's modulus is lowered while at the same time, T_g (the temperature of the glass transition point) is raised. This results in a decreased Young's modulus. Silicon molecules become mixed with the epoxy molecules. There is increasingly widespread use of this altered epoxy mixed polymer structure. Figure 9 shows examples of the decreased stress that results from improved resins [2].

Usually, when the Young's modulus is lowered further, there is deterioration in the resin's heat resistance. It is hoped that some sort of a compromise in terms of mounting technology will emerge so as to lower the temperature during substrate mounting. A specific example would be the use of a conductive adhesive agent. In addition to lowering the Young's modulus, another effective method of relaxing stress on the chip is the use of high density silica filler to lower the resin's thermal expansion. This, however, can hamper formability during molding so for the most part the current limit is $1 \times 10^{-5}/°C$.

For compact packages, particularly for packages using resin with low coefficients of expansion, there is a tendency to keep the coefficient of thermal expansion close to that of the chip itself and to have an insulating gap between the package and the printed substrate. As a result, the question of decreasing the thermal stress on the leads' soldered areas becomes even more important. In terms of the package, lead shape techniques such as butt joint leads are possible. In terms of mounting, necessary improvements include the selection of low-expansion substrates compatible with the application or mounting process at hand and the optimal selection of either resin type and weight or land dimension.

Hermeticity

Even compact, high-pin-count packages have sufficient reliability in terms of operations at normal levels of high temperature and high humidity, owing to advances in resins. A recent problem, though, is the so-called popcorn phenomenon in which the moisture absorbed by the package causes it to crack from the thermal stress of mounting. The water in the mold resin suddenly expands because of the heat of soldering. This creates cracks in the resin, whose adhesion is normally difficult to maintain, while in the lead frame, gaps are created between the die pad and the epoxy. Figure 10 shows this mechanism.

Physical values of epoxy resin

Item Type	a_1 $(10\text{-}5/°C)$	T_g $(°C)$	E_1 (kg/mm^2)
Epoxy A	2.5	170	1,550
Epoxy B	2.1	165	1,550
Epoxy C	2.1	150	1,550
Epoxy D	2.1	145	1,100

a_1 : Linear expansion coefficient below T_g temp.

T_g : Glass transition temperature

E_1 : Young's modulus

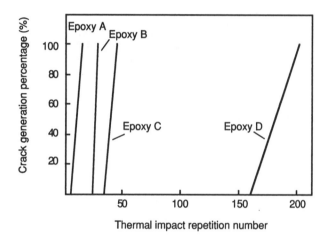

Fig. 9 An example of a decrease in resin stress as seen from package cracks caused by thermal shock. The thermal shock is $-196°$ C (30 s) $\Leftrightarrow 260°$ C (30 s). The package is a 16-pin dual in-line package.

For TSOP and other compact packages, sufficient attention has been paid to prevention of the popcorn effect in terms of resin selection, the dimensional ratio of the chip to the package's external dimensions, and better adhesion between the die pad and the resin. In addition to these measures, chips are usually packaged in moisture-proof containers for shipping.

For users, it is recommended that vapor phase soldering and air flow methods be used to lower mounting temperature. Moreover, baking must be performed after resin sealing and before mounting.

(a) Humidity is absorbed

(b) Moisture condenses

(c) Moisture expands due to
thermal stress during
mounting

(d) Resin cracks

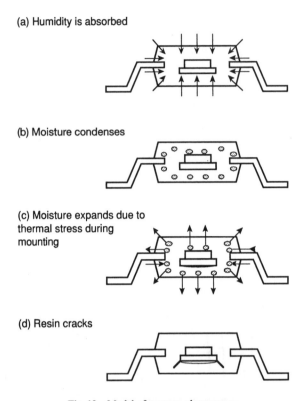

Fig. 10   Model of popcorn phenomenon.

Heat

For equipment that does not use fans, such as some household electrical
devices, the heat generated in the LSI is distributed to the substrate through the
package leads. For computers in which chip and board mountings are of
extremely high density, fans are normally used to blow off heat from the package
surfaces. Nonetheless improvements in terms of heat diffusion from the surface
of the package itself are advocated [3]. Internally buried copper plates improve
heat diffusion as do copper plates exposed to the package surface. These methods
are applicable for LSIs up to the level of several watts.

In order to develop packages with superb heat diffusion characteristics,
design and manufacturing techniques must be used to obtain a balance between
the thermal expansion of the various structural materials. The development of a
package with high heat diffusion characteristics beyond the simple addition of
cooling fins is awaited. This achievement requires an integration of packaging
technology and equipment assembly technology. In terms of mounting technol-

ogy, starting with laser soldering, developments are underway of bonding methods that greatly reduce thermal stress to the package itself. The implementation of these methods is being rapidly promoted.

CONCLUSION

In addition to developments in LSI package manufacturing and mounting process technology, there has been progress toward the completion and standardization of SMT LSI package line-ups. As evidenced by the joint EIAJ-JEDEC meetings, the movements toward international standards, though not totally unified, are getting stronger. The beginnings can be seen of a struggle to deal with that great obstacle, the inch-millimeter dimensional unit controversy.

It is hoped that progress in standardization for both users and makers will continue and that its basis will rest upon a coordination of package and mounting technology.

REFERENCES

[1] Takehara, "Latest Trends in VLSI Packages and Design Technology '90," *Technology Information Center,* pp. 91–113, January 1990.

[2] Takehara, "Latest Trends in Package Technology," *Semicon News,* pp. 29–36, March 1989.

[3] "A Resin Sealed QFP Adaptable to 4W That Has Great Savings in Power Consumption and a High Pin Count," *Nikkei Microdevices,* no. 51 pp. 91–99, September 1989.

Latest Trends in Hybrid IC Multilayer Substrates

Hideo Takamizawa

NEC Corp.

TRENDS IN PACKAGING TECHNOLOGY

As we become an increasingly advanced, information-oriented society, the data processing equipment market will expand in response to a wide diversity of needs.

Data processing equipment is improving in functionality and performance and spurring the development of user-friendly, compact products. These include input devices such as electronic still cameras and HDTV camcorders and output devices such as flat panel displays (especially liquid crystal displays), large plasma displays, electronic photographic printers, and high-speed portable facsimiles. In storage devices, we expect new magnetic recording devices, optical disks, and smart cards, while in data processing equipment there will be new computers, TV screens, electronic notebooks, personal computers, and word processors. Major advances are anticipated in automotive and consumer electronics products as well.

These products will require not only the development of integrated circuits (ICs) and large scale integration (LSI) electronic components but a comprehensive design and packaging technology as well. Packaging methods such as hybrid ICs (HIC)—which involve printed circuit board mounting and ceramic substrate technology—have developed playing a major role as mounting substrates. Figure 1 shows the trend in packaging technology.

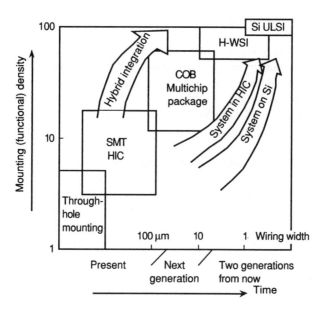

Fig. 1 Trends in mounting technology.

Packaging technology has changed from through-hole mounting to the currently used chip components and surface mount technology (SMT), and is now changing to system-oriented HICs. SMT has presented satisfactory results as a production technology that meets the demand for high-density packaging, low cost, and short turnaround time. What type of technology can replace SMT? From the viewpoint of technology, a replacement must meet the requirements for the high-density packaging of thin and compact end products, composite modules for increased functionality, and increasingly higher levels of speed and capacity.

Chip on board (COB), a method of mounting bare chips directly onto the substrate, is one of the technologies expected to fulfill the packaging needs described above. Interconnection and substrate technologies for ICs and LSIs are being developed in earnest for practical applications. Functions demanding high performance and large capacity naturally require the capability of multichip packaging to assemble many ICs and LSI chips onto a substrate. In this sense, multichip packaging (MCP) (or multichip module–MCM) of bare chips is the technology that will succeed SMT. The assembly of multiple chips onto a substrate requires fine-pattern and multilayer wiring technology. This paper will primarily discuss technological trends in multilayer ceramics for HIC.

TRENDS IN MULTILAYER SUBSTRATE TECHNOLOGY

New mounting substrates must meet the demand for high density packaging, high speed and functionality, and low thermal resistance. Substrate materials have diversified to include not only conventional alumina ceramics but glass ceramic, low temperature fired substrates, highly conductive aluminum nitride substrates, and multilayer polyimides. Figure 2 shows the requirements for substrates and the corresponding technologies. Table 1 shows main multilayer substrate technologies. In the past, most multilayer HIC substrates had fewer than ten layers and were made with a thick film method in which wiring and insulating pastes were alternately screen printed onto the alumina substrate. The cofired green sheet method using alumina is also widely used as a highly accurate multilayering technique. The problem with the former is that it limits the wiring pitch and number of layers, while the latter has a high dielectric constant, incompatible coefficient of thermal expansion with silicon, and a high conductor resistance. These characteristics are not suited to high speed, high integration LSI packaging.

To cope with these problems, new methods are being developed and put into practical use. Among them is a low-temperature-fired multilayer glass ceramic substrate, which has a low dielectric constant and can accommodate silver, copper, and gold low-resistance conductors. Others include a thin film–thick film combination that aims to reduce the dielectric constant and is capable of fine patterns, and a polyimide fine patterned multilayer technology. These multilayer substrate technologies will be introduced in the next section.

RECENT MULTILAYER HIC SUBSTRATES

Low-Temperature-Fired Ceramic Multilayer Substrate

The low-temperature-fired ceramic substrate is made of a composite material consisting mainly of a borosilicate glass and a ceramic such as alumina, and is fired at 800 to 1,000°C. As Figure 2 indicates, it is superior to the alumina substrate in a variety of ways: its low dielectric constant makes high-speed device packaging possible; its coefficient of thermal expansion is similar to silicon, relieving stress during mounting; low-resistance conductors such as silver, copper and gold can be used; and capacitors and resistors with a high dielectric constant can be built into the layers.

Figure 3 shows the relationship between signal propagation delay time and dielectric constant. In one report, a ceramic material with a dielectric constant of 3.9 produced a delay time approximately 40% less than when mounted on alumina [1]. In addition, glass ceramic has approximately the same mechanical

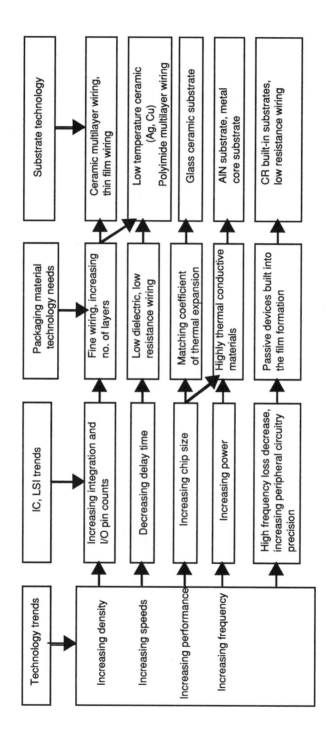

Fig. 2 Trends in integrated circuit and large scale integration requirements and hybrid IC substrate technology.

TABLE 1 The Main Multilayer Wiring Substrate Materials

	Thick film multilayer method	Green sheet multilayer cofired method (alumina)	Green sheet multilayer cofired method (glass ceramic)	Green sheet multilayer co-fired method (aluminum nitride)	Thin film–thick film mixed method	Polyimide multilayer method
Substrate	Alumina	—	—	—	Alumina/glass ceramic	Alumina
Insulation film	Alumina/glass	Alumina	Glass ceramic	Aluminum nitride	Glass ceramic*	Polyimide
Wiring material	W, Mo/Ag•Pd, Cu	Mo, W	Ag, Ag•Pd, Au, Cu	W	Au	Au, Cu
Wiring width	100 μm	100 μm	80 μm	100 μm	25–40 μm	25–70 μm
Wiring spacing	150 μm	150 μm	150 μm	150 μm	50–70 μm	50–150 μm
Wiring formation	Printing	Printing	Printing	Printing	Sputter/etching	Sputter/ etching, etc.
Through-hole diameter	Above 300 μm	150–300 μm	150–300 μm	150–300 μm	100–200 μm	50–150 μm
No. of layers possible	2–10 layers	2–50 layers	2–50 layers	2–50 layers	2–10 layers	2–10 layers
Characteristics	Simple process	Reliability	Low ε, low resistance conductor	High thermal conductivity	Fine wiring	Low ε, fine process

*Photosetting paste

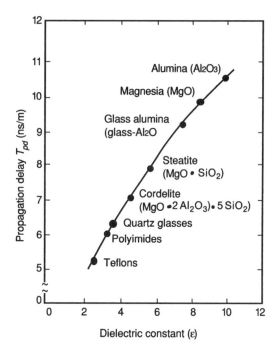

Fig. 3 Signal propagation delay time and dielectric constant.

strength as alumina. Silver, gold, and copper conductors have been developed as a multilayer substrate for multichip packages in large computers and are in practical use [2]. In the future, it will be important to match the substrate's coefficient of thermal expansion with silicon when LSI chips are directly mounted onto the substrate for high density packaging. The need increases especially as the chip size increases. While it is possible for glass ceramic to have a coefficient of thermal expansion similar to silicon, glass ceramic's low thermal conductivity requires matching it to the metal fin if the package is so equipped. Table 2 shows the characteristics of low-temperature-fired ceramic multilayer substrates [3]. A new technology is under development for compact substrates in high density packaging for high functionality. In this technique, passive devices are formed within the substrate. The realization of this technique will make possible compact end products with a high level of functionality. It will also offer significant advantages in production because of the reduction in the number of components and packaging process steps. Recently, this method has gained attention as an integrated packaging method without a boundary between the substrate and component [4], [5]. In the future, needs will drive the development of optimal designs and highly reliable process technologies that take the technology level into consideration.

TABLE 2 Low Temperature Ceramic Substrate Characteristics and Specifications (continued next page)

Characteristic	Item		Characteristic value	Value relative to Al_2O_3
Electrical characteristics	Dielectric constant	(1 MHz)	3.9–8.5	9.0–10
	Dielectric loss, tan δ (%)		0.01–0.3	0.01
	Insulation resistance	(Ω · cm)	1×10^{14}–2×10^{15}	$\approx 1 \times 10^{14}$
Thermal characteristics	Coefficient of thermal expansion	(× 106/°C)	1.9–8.0	7–7.5
	Thermal conductivity	(W/M•K)	2–8	15–20
Mechanical strength	Resistance to breakage	(kg/cm^2)	1,400–3,000	$\approx$3,000
Physical performance	Specific gravity	(g/cm^3)	2.1–4.6	$\approx$3.8
	Warp	(μm/50 mm)	≥15	
	Surface roughness	(μmRa)	0.1–2.0	
Sintering characteristics	Sintering temperature	(°C)	800–1,050	≥1,500
	Shrinkage	%	12–20	
Wiring conductor			Ad•Pd, Ag•Au, Cu	W, Mo

TABLE 2 Substrate Production Specifications

| | Multilayer ceramic substrate specifications | | |
Specification	Experimental range	Postulated range	Comments
Wiring width (μm)	100–500	70 minimum	Au, Ag•Pd
Wiring spacing (μm)	100–1,000	100 minimum	Au, Ag•Pd
Via hole (μm)	200–1,000	120 minimum	
Via hole spacing (μm)	≥500	≥3,000	
Green sheet thickness	50–500	30–1,000	
Number of layers	41 maximum	≈60(?)	
Substrate size (mm)	50–100 square	≈150	

Thin Film–Thick Film Combination Ceramic Multilayer Substrate

The one-chip module, which is in demand for equipment including mainframe computers and image processing machines, needs a greater wiring density to increase its mounting density for high-pin-count very large scale integration (VLSI) chips as well as multichip modules that integrate a central processing unit with memory and controller. One alternative is a method that repeats the following process: thin film formation by sputtering; fine pattern formation by photolithography; insulating layer formation (fine via formation) by photosetting insulating paste. Depending on the packaging requirement, fine multilayer patterns can be formed either on a cofired ceramic substrate or on a single alumina substrate.

Figure 4 shows the structure of an LSI mounting substrate for mainframe computers [6]. Fine patterns (mainly signal lines) are formed on a low-temperature-fired ceramic substrate. Titanium (Ti) and palladium (Pd) are sputtered onto the surface of the substrate and the substrate is exposed and developed. The patterns are then selectively plated with gold. The conductor is approximately 30 μm wide. Subsequently, photosetting insulating paste is screen printed to form an insulating layer and fired at 850°C to 900°C, as shown in Fig. 5. Vias with a diameter of approximately 50 μm can be formed in 50 μm-thick film. Fine multilayer patterns are formed by repeating these steps [7]. This is an effective multilayer substrate capable of high-speed signal propagation.

Polyimide Multilayer Substrate

Because glass epoxy or polyimide multilayer printed substrates are sometimes used for HICs, the definition of HIC substrate is not clear. In this section,

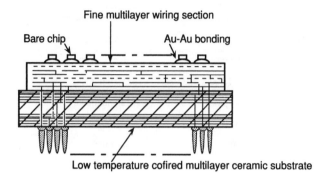

Fig. 4   Hybrid multilayer ceramic substrate structure cross-section.

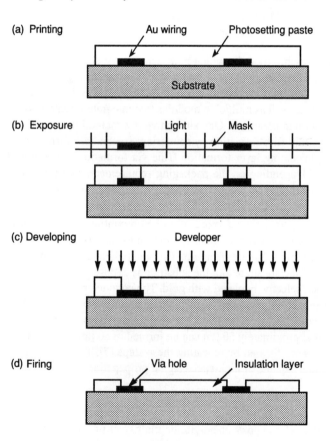

Fig. 5   Hybrid multilayer ceramic substrate structure cross-section.

however, we introduce multilayer substrates whether ceramic, silicon, or metal (including lead frames) that use polyimide coating for insulating layers. The polyimide method is being developed as part of a technology that uses a high-speed LSI device as a substrate to increase the mounting density of multichip packages by taking advantage of the low dielectric constant and fine patterning. In the past, this method was used to achieve planar and smooth silicon substrates but it is now used for VLSI packaging for mainframe computers that require high-speed device packaging. Table 3 shows the structural specifications of this multilayer substrate and Fig. 6 shows the mounting substrate [8]. This substrate has ten 20,000-gate VLSIs and is 22.5 cm square. The mounting density is high at 4,000 gates/cm^2. A copper polyimide multilayer substrate for VCRs has also been developed, with 20 μm-wide conductors with 20 μm spacing for a mounting density ten times that of thick-film hybrid multilayer substrates [9]. Both photosensitive and nonphotosensitive polyimides are used.

Fig. 6 Multilayer substrate for mounting very large scale integration chip.

TABLE 3   Multilayer Ceramic Substrate for VLSI (for the SX-3
Supercomputer)

Ceramic substrate dimensions	225 mm × 225 mm × 5.5 mm
Wiring width/pitch	25 µm/75 µm
Number of wiring layers	8 layers (4 signal layers)
I/O pin count	11,540 pins
Fine wiring technology	
Wiring layer	Thin film wiring
Insulation layer	Polyimide resin (dielectric constant ≈ 3.5)
Ceramic substrate	Cofired thick-film multilayer ceramic substrate
Number of LSI chips mounted (maximum)	100 chips
Heat diffusion method	Conductive water cooling
Thermal resistance from the LSI pn junction to the coolant water	≈ 0.6°C/W
LSI pn junction temperature	≈ 50–55°C
Exothermic density	7.9 W/cm^2

Aluminum Nitride Multilayer Substrate

Aluminum nitride ceramic has a thermal conductivity similar to metal aluminum (240W/m•K), and is being anticipated as a high-integration, high-power VLSI mounting substrate. Presently, it is being evaluated for multilayer packages for bipolar LSIs and metal oxide semiconductor chips in single-chip pin grid arrays and quad flat packages. The aluminum nitride ceramic is also under development as a HIC multilayer substrate for high-power microwave amplifiers and automotive and high-current electronics applications. A seven-layer substrate has been announced that has a coefficient of thermal expansion close to silicon and uses tungsten for the conductor layer [10]. In the future, commercialization of such substrates will be faced with issues such as cost and the reliability of interconnections.

CONCLUSION

Unlike the simple circuit substrates of the past, in developing HICs it is important to optimize the functioning of each unit in terms of the performance, cost, and reliability of the entire system. In the multichip packaging of ICs and LSIs, the key hardware factor is the development of multilayer wiring substrate technology with high density mounting, fine pattern wiring, and high functionality.

Because hybrid integration technology can realize system functions unattainable by means of monolithic semiconductors, its importance will increase as we strive for a system-in-HIC in the future.

REFERENCES

[1] Kara et al., *Proc. 1989 Japan IEMT Symposium*, p. 26, 1989.

[2] *Nikkei Microdevices*, no. 48, p. 38, June 1989.

[3] Takamizawa, *HYBRIDS*, vol. 1, no. 3, 1985.

[4] Tokaka et al., *Proc. Symp. Microelectronics*, 1988.

[5] Utsumi et al., *Mat. Res. Soc. Symp.* vol. 72, 1986.

[6] Doya et al., *Proc. Symp. Second Microelectronics (MES)*, p. 197, 1987.

[7] H. Takamizawa et al., *Proc. ISHM*, p. 74, 1985.

[8] *Nikkei Electronics*, no. 472, May 1, 1989.

[9] Takada et al., *Proc. Symp. Microelectronics*, p. 540, 1988.

[10] Hamaguchi et al., *Proc. Symp. Second Microelectronics (MES)*, p. 185, 1987.

Interconnect Technology for Achieving Small Size, Lightweight Camcorders

Kenji Toyofuku

Sony Corp.

INTRODUCTION

A passport-size camcorder, CCD-TR55 (Fig. 1) was introduced to the market in June, 1989. This product reflects Sony's commitment to miniaturization and an attempt to create a new market for 8-mm camcorders. It offers a lifestyle that enables users to enjoy carefree videotaping and viewing regardless of the location. The product concept was developed for traveling.

Since the arrival of the CCD-TR55, camcorders have not only become popular, but have also contributed to revitalizing a maturing VCR market. This has affected the acceleration of technological development for compact and lightweight equipment in recent new audiovisual (AV) equipment. The new market for compact, lightweight products also includes products such as electronic notebooks, notebook computers, and cellular phones.

As the trend toward compact and lightweight products continues, the introduction of more complex products offering user-friendliness and aimed at a wider variety of applications will provide growth in the market. One of the key technologies that will make these product design goals possible is high density mounting technology. This paper will primarily discuss the high density mounting technology in the CCD-TR55 and the interconnect design of the four-layer substrate in particular.

Fig. 1   The 8-mm video camcorder model CCD-TR55.

CHANGES IN INTERCONNECT METHODS

A variety of interconnect and soldering methods have been developed for changing product needs. Figure 2 shows the changes that have occurred in interconnect methods, mounting density, type of components, and substrate specifications for an 8-mm camcorder.

In the past, a dip method of soldering lead-type components was the leading method in AV equipment. However, chip components, miniaturized components, and interconnect technologies have been developed specifically for compact AV equipment, and the interconnect method has changed to incorporate a double-sided substrate and reflow soldering. The CCD-TR55 uses this double-sided substrate and reflow soldering. Indeed, the unifying characteristic of interconnect methods used in all of the latest products is the full-scale adoption of surface mount technology.

HIGH-DENSITY MOUNTING IN THE TR55

Substrate Layout

The main substrate of the CCD-TR55 contains one camera block substrate and one video block substrate. The camera block substrate uses one hybrid inte-

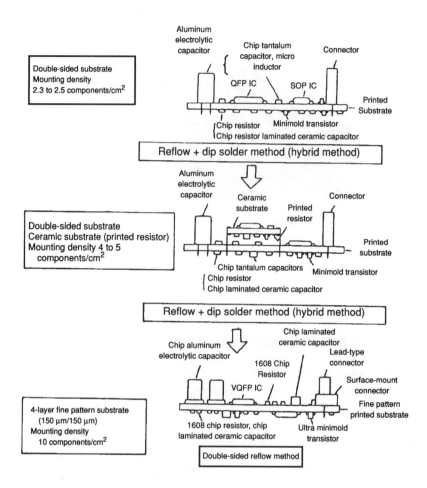

Fig. 2   The changing interconnect methods of 8-mm video camcorders.

grated circuit (IC) with a ceramic substrate for heat dissipation. The video block substrate includes a signal processing (Y&C) circuit, system controller, and servo circuit.

In the newly developed main substrate, there are four thin glass polyimide layers. Compact chip components and devices, which will be discussed later in this paper, are also used. These substrates, components, and devices were introduced to achieve high density mounting (Fig. 3). The average mounting density is 10 components per cm^2. The substrate area inside the system was also reduced to half of the previous model.

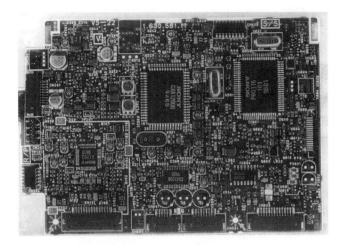

Fig. 3 The CCD-TR55 mounting substrate.

Components and Devices

The key point of high density mounting is to reduce the substrate area occupied by components. This means making smaller components and devices and packing them together tightly, as well as reducing the number of components.

As the component configuration in Table 1 indicates, CCD-TR55 contains a large number of compact components such as 1608 CR chip components to achieve an average mounting density of 10 components per cm^2. Integrated circuits with a lead pitch of 0.5 mm, called VQFP, have been adapted to reduce the area occupied by components. Also, the number of components has been reduced by using composite chip resistors and composite transistors.

Other compact components include connectors with narrower pitch and semi-fixed resistors. Efforts are underway to reduce the number of semi-fixed resistors and minimize adjustments in the circuitry by increasing the current.

By redesigning irregular components such as connectors, filters, and crystals into surface mount devices (SMD), 98% of all components used can be mounted automatically. The percentage of components that are mounted automatically is an extremely important factor in improving the surface mount quality on a high density mounting substrate.

Thin, Four-Layer Fine Pattern Substrate

As Table 1 indicates, the CCD-TR55 has approximately 2,200 circuit components. Components occupy 80% of the main substrate's surface area. The four-layer fine pattern substrate was developed to improve the efficiency of the pattern

TABLE 1   List of Components Used in the CCD-TR55

Component	Count
1608 chip component resistor	780
Composite chip resistor	70
1608 chip component capacitor	490
2125, 3216 chip CR	180
MM transistor (incl. transistor pairs)	103
SMM transistor	92
VQFP-IC	11
VSOP-IC	7
Other ICs	39
Total	≈2,200

wiring. Figure 4 shows the four layers of the substrate and Fig. 5 is a diagram of a cross section of the substrate.

This newly developed thin, four-layer substrate is 0.6 mm thick and has a wiring pattern design rule with 150 μm line width and 150 μm spacing. The through-hole land diameter is 0.5 mm and the through-hole diameter is 0.35 mm.

The thermal shock through-hole conductivity test (i.e., hot oil test), insulation test, and migration resistance test were conducted to determine the reliability of the substrate. After modifying and improving the glass cloth treatment solution, test results were similar or even superior to those of currently used four-layer substrates that are 1.2 to 6 mm thick. The resist was supplied accurately between IC lands on the substrate by using liquid resist and improving the resist alignment technique. In addition, the surface was treated with a newly developed preflux with high thermal resistance. These measures improved the solder wettability of the copper (i.e., the land) during reflow, thereby substantially reducing soldering defects such as bridging and missing solder.

EFFECT ON COMPACTNESS AND WEIGHT REDUCTION

Compactness

Compared with 2125 chip components, the 1608 CR components occupy approximately 23 cm^2 less space. This corresponds to a substrate size reduction of approximately 11.5 cm^2. In addition, the use of VQFP ICs reduced the mount-

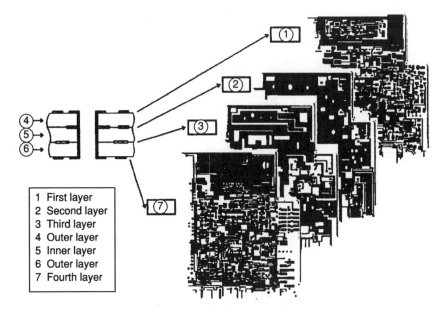

1 First layer
2 Second layer
3 Third layer
4 Outer layer
5 Inner layer
6 Outer layer
7 Fourth layer

Fig. 4 Diagram of the 4-layer substrate.

ing area by approximately 21 cm^2, which corresponds to a substrate size reduction of 10.5 cm^2. Thus, the use of both 1608 CR chip components and VQFP-ICs enabled the substrate area to be reduced by approximately 10%.

Weight Reduction

The CCD-TR55's weight has also been reduced by approximately 6 grams using 1608 CR chip components compared with using 2125 chip components. The replacement of QFP ICs with VQFP ICs reduced the weight by approximately 8 grams. Furthermore, approximately 30 grams was taken off by using the newly developed thin, four-layer substrate (with a thickness of 0.6 mm) instead of the existing 1.2 mm-thick, four-layer substrate.

The total weight reduction using 1608 CR chip components, VQFP ICs, and the thin, four-layer substrate amounts to approximately 5.6%. This is approximately 35% of the weight of the total substrate assembly.

PRINTED WIRING BOARD DESIGN TECHNOLOGY

In the past, printed circuit board designs were prepared by drawing a rough draft by hand, and the original artwork for production was created by block copy. This

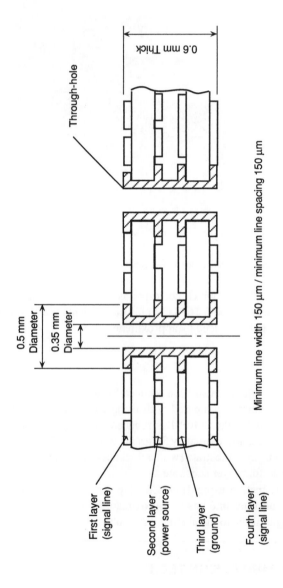

Through-hole

0.6 mm Thick

0.5 mm Diameter

0.35 mm Diameter

First layer (signal line)

Second layer (power source)

Third layer (ground)

Fourth layer (signal line)

Minimum line width 150 μm / minimum line spacing 150 μm

Fig. 5 Cross-section of the 4-layer substrate.

design method was inadequate for fine patterning because of its poor accuracy. Now, computer-aided design (CAD) is widely used for high density mounting and multilayer substrates. A new CAD system was introduced to design the multilayer fine pattern substrates in the CCD-TR55. Simulations were performed with the CAD system to determine the component layout and height limitations so as to obtain an optimal component layout for the given circuit characteristics.

The substrate design of the CCD-TR55 incorporated an interactive approach between the component layout and wiring connections. After the design was completed, the CAD system performed a connection check (net check) against the schematic diagram, parts list, and a layout pattern diagram. Gap checks in the wiring pattern were also performed using the DRC function of CAD. The CAD net check and DRC function eliminate defects in the substrate design such as false or missing connections and narrow gaps that are substandard. The CAD system contributes greatly to improving substrate design quality and reducing design time. Figure 6 shows the substrate design flow using CAD.

SMT involves difficulties not present in previous lead-type packages, and as the mounting density increases, so too does the level of technology needed to place and solder components. Beginning with the circuit and wiring pattern design stage, design standards must be set for pattern and land dimensional design and component alignment and spacing to fully utilize the knowledge gained thus far in such mounting technologies as soldering. High density mounting substrate design standards have been rebuilt and reset to achieve good solderability, product quality and productivity, and to make effective use of CAD design.

By connecting this CAD system to the computer-aided manufacturing (CAM) system that mounts components, the design time required for programming the mounting process of the automated placer, previously done manually, has been greatly reduced. Furthermore, the data on mounting that can now be collected help to improve product quality.

ASSEMBLY PROCESS

Figure 7 shows the assembly process flow for the CCD-TR55, which will be discussed briefly in this section. An appropriate amount of solder paste is screen printed onto prescribed locations of the printed circuit substrate using a stencil. The amount of solder being printed is controlled by the stencil thickness, finish of the stencil openings, solder paste material, and printing conditions. It is necessary to thoroughly understand and control the particle shape, solder particle distribution, and viscosity of the solder paste to achieve a good, high precision solder print. Defects in soldering, such as tombstones, are possible if the amount of solder, reflow conditions, and land design standards are not properly controlled.

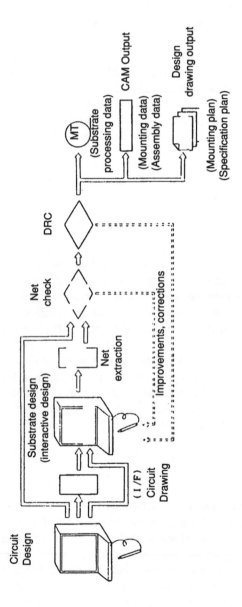

Fig. 6 Substrate design flow.

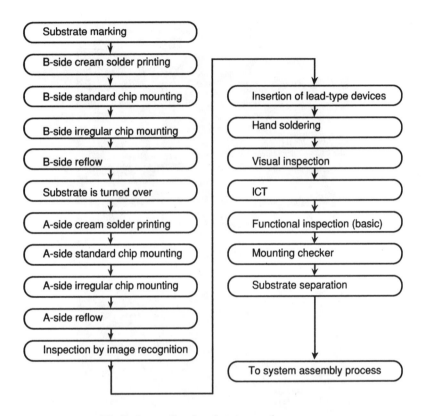

Fig. 7   Process flow for substrate mounting process.

Sony is using solder paste with spherical particles, as shown in Fig. 8, and is achieving excellent printing results.

The high density mounting of diversified components using SMT requires that thermal stress be minimized during assembly. A solder paste for low temperature soldering has been developed to meet this requirement. Standard chip components are placed on the substrate using a high speed one-by-one automated component-placing machine. A change in the nozzle configuration of the placing machine has improved the centering of devices. The use of the parts cassette classifier improves the placement accuracy of 1608 chip components.

Efforts are being made to improve mounting quality. An image recognition system has been added to the automatic placement machine to identify and expel defective ICs based on their lead shape, as well as to improve the positioning accuracy of components.

As explained above, the CCD-TR55 uses a double-sided substrate reflow soldering method. A hot air reflow oven is used to ensure a uniform temperature

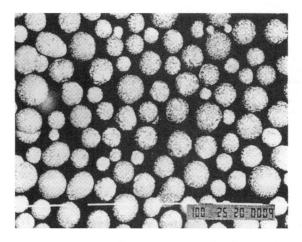

(a) Spherical particles

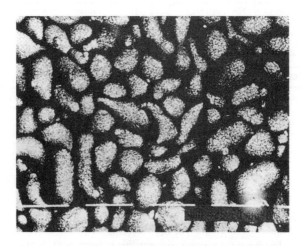

(b) Irregular particles

Fig. 8 Particle shapes for the low-melting-point cream solder.

distribution across the mounting substrate and to reduce thermal stress to components and devices. Whereas a conventional infrared radiation (IR) reflow oven
can have a temperature variation of 50 to 60° C on the substrate, the hot air reflow
oven has a controller that keeps the temperature variation to within 20° C. The
thermal stress on components and devices has been reduced using the hot air
reflow oven, resulting in a decrease in the number of soldering defects and an
increase in the reliability of the soldering.

FUTURE PROSPECTS

This paper has discussed the interconnect technology used in our 8-mm camcorder. In the future, AV equipment manufacturers will develop even lighter, more compact products in response to strong demand. Improved interconnect technology is necessary to achieve the higher density mounting needed to cope with this demand. Future developments are expected in the following areas: extremely compact CR chip components, miniaturized or fine-pitch general purpose components and ICs, and fine patterning and higher counts of layers in printed wiring substrates. For example, 1005 chip components are beginning to be used in some instances. Also, the JPCA show indicates a trend toward fine patterning in printed wiring boards.

In the future, the most important issues in high density mounting technology will be to attain high quality and reliability. Toward this end, interconnect technologies such as fine pitch soldering, anisotropic conductive film, and ultraviolet curing resins are being developed and commercialized. Rather than developing individual technologies, it is important that all the basic technologies are developed together, including interconnect design, component technology, mounting technology, factory automation, and inspection technology.

REFERENCES

[1] Ohshima, Toyofuki, "Compact technology in consumer AV equipment," *J. Inst. Television Engineers,* vol. 43, no. 6, pp. 583–586, June 1989.

[2] Toyofuku, "Design, interconnection and inspection of multilayer substrates for various products: The 8 mm camcorder," *Mounting Technology,* Joho Chosakai, vol. 15, no. 11, pp. 34–38, November 1989.

[3] Toyofuku: "Assembly of 8mm camcorders," *INJ/ET/ADEE Seminar,* Kogyo Chosakai, p. 9, January 1990.

[4] Toyofuku: "Electronic components and packaging technology," *Nikkan Kogyo Shinbun,* pp. 25–27, March 30, 1990.

The Transformation of Interconnect Technology

Hideyuki Nishida

IBM Japan Ltd.

INTRODUCTION

Demand from users with respect to electronic components, particularly large scale integration (LSI) packages has increased rapidly in recent times. Progress in semiconductor technology has promoted higher levels of integration for LSI devices at a furious pace and brought on an era of lighter, thinner, shorter, and smaller products. Mounting technology has been influenced by this trend and is resulting in development of new techniques, equipment, and materials for the surface mounting of very small chip components and high density packages. Surface mount technology (SMT) has been around long enough to be considered a conventional mounting technology. There are two approaches to take in making the next step toward a new mounting technology (e.g., toward higher density): 1) reevaluate the conventional method, improve it, and aim for the next higher dimension, and 2) adopt new methods and materials.

The interconnect method used in Company S's new video camcorder is indisputably an extreme example of the first approach. The microbonding technology announced by Company M, or the new interconnection technology using resin materials introduced by a number of watch and calculator makers are examples of the second approach. Once we have a comprehensive grasp of semiconductor, substrate, component, and mounting technologies; understand the present situation; and consider the prospects we have to determine which approach is in fact is the correct one. In this paper, we will investigate this question by focusing on trends in mounting components and changes taking place in interconnect methods and bonding technology and, having grasped the present situation, determine what the future issues are.

TRENDS IN MOUNTING COMPONENTS

Extremely small chip components and quad flat packages (QFPs) with a very fine pitch are causing new problems for mounting technology. The next target for chip components is to shift from 1608 to 1005 components (1005 refers to the 1.0 mm × 0.5 mm size), while QFPs are changing from 0.5 mm pitch to 0.3 mm pitch. From the standpoint of practical use, while there is debate as to whether 0.3-mm pitch QFPs and 1005 components actually are more competitive than their predecessors, it is common knowledge that these represent the current trends in mounting. For instance, with regard to LSI packages, users (i.e., the designer or system maker who selects the LSI package and designs the mounting substrate or product) demand the following:

1. accommodation of the increasing functionality and higher performance of LSIs;
2. conservation of space and allowance for size reduction (especially for thinner and lighter end products);
3. high quality, reliability, and an established record in the market;
4. low cost (cost performance improves because of greater functionality and higher performance at the same cost);
5. custom specifications (suited to specific application); and
6. ease of mounting, repairing, and automating.

These demands on packaging can be met in the following ways:

1. higher density at the LSI device level (i.e., greater functionality of logic devices, increased capacity of memory devices) or increasing chip size;
2. packages that are smaller, lighter, and have finer features;
3. customization of package specifications;
4. development of new methods and equipment to mount new packages and provision of technical support to the user;
5. joint development of new materials and packages with the user; and
6. guaranteeing product quality and reliability by screening and function testing at the component level.

The increase in the mounting density of electronic circuit components is highly dependent on the increased integration of semiconductor devices themselves. As demonstrated by the development of DRAM memories from 256K to 1M, to 4M, to 16M, and to 64M, device integration knows no bounds, which complicates mounting. Logic devices are increasing in speed and functionality while their lead counts rise. This trend is especially apparent in bipolar ICs. Figure 1 shows the card and board (mounting substrate) of the IBM System 370/Model 168. Figure 1a shows the trend in the number of CMOS and bipolar semiconductor device circuits, trend in DRAM devices, and the predicted growth trend according to Rent's rule. Figure 1b shows the trend in the actual and predicted pin counts of IBM's first-level packaging. It is clear from these figures that the pin count will increase substantially as the level of integration of the semiconductor circuits rises. With practical use in mind, higher pin counts can be met in the following ways:

1. increased level of integration while maintaining same chip size to decrease the pin pitch (in this case, narrower pitch means that the semiconductor's ground rule is changed, or finer features at the chip level are required);
2. if the semiconductor's ground rule is left unchanged, the LSI chip size must be increased; and
3. the I/O pins can be placed not only at the chip's periphery but also in a matrix array over the entire surface.

Although the quality of high purity silicon wafer base material for LSI devices has improved recently, with the complexity of semiconductor processes increasing on a daily basis, yields are better for smaller chip sizes. Thus, one of the issues to be considered is the attainment of higher density by means of finer pitch.

CHANGES IN PACKAGING

If we looked inside newer products such as personal computers and video camcorders, we would find a substrate crammed with miniature chip components, thin-profile SMT packages, and very-fine-pitch QFPs. It was not long ago that these leadless chip components and SMT packages were discrete wire components and DIP packages inserted into through holes. Compared with components with leads, the leadless components and SMT packages have made a major contribution by reducing floating capacity, decreasing wire length, and improving propagation delay, thereby extracting maximal performance from LSI chips. As evidenced by chip on board (COB) and chip on glass (COG) methods, the recent trend in packaging is blurring the distinction between first- and second-level packaging. Figure 2a shows the change in packaging forms, and Fig. 2b shows both the technology accompanying the shift from System 3033 to 308X/309X series, and the effect on cycle time of changes in packaging. As Fig. 2b indicates,

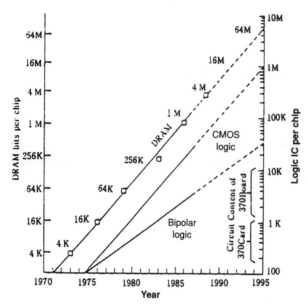

(a) Number of circuits per semiconductor device—actual and predicted

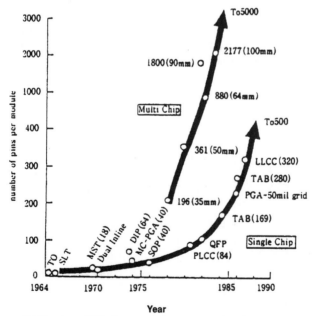

(b) Number of I/O pins per package—actual and predicted

Fig. 1 Trend in level of integration of large scale integration (LSI) devices for mainframe computers.

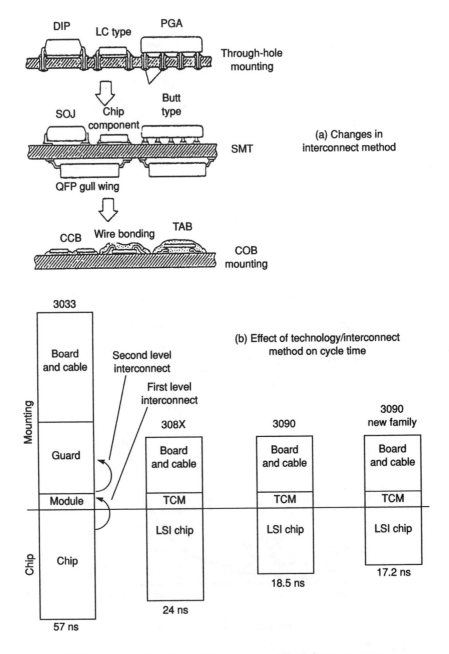

Fig. 2   Interconnect methods and the performance of mainframe computers.

by removing the secondary packaging level of mounting the LSI packages onto the substrate, and mounting the thermoconduction module (TCM) directly onto the motherboard, the cycle time was reduced drastically. By removing packaging levels in this way, it may eventually be possible to install all the necessary electronic circuitry onto one silicon wafer or silicon chip.

CURRENT STATE OF INTERCONNECT TECHNOLOGY

Figure 3 shows the types of bonding methods for first-level LSI packaging and their features. In place of wire bonding, which has been widely used, attention has been on tape automated bonding (TAB) and controlled collapse bonding (CCB). As stated previously, this change is a result of the trend toward higher pin counts and narrower pitch. By reducing the pitch of I/O pads around the periphery of LSIs, TAB has become suitable for narrow pitch bonding of small LSI chips with about 500 pins. Controlled collapse bonding, which can have pads on the entire LSI chip surface including the active area, eliminates the wires and leads of first-level packaging and directly connects the chip to the substrate, thereby enabling noise control. The minimal wiring length also has the effect of improving electrical characteristics. Therefore, it is ideal for mounting high speed devices with advanced functions. In contrast to bonding of metal to metal (i.e., inorganic materials) new bonding methods have recently been commercialized that use organic materials such as adhesives and conductive rubber.

FUTURE ISSUES

The trend in LSI devices toward higher levels of integration and higher pin counts creates new issues for mounting technology. The development theme for the future will be to establish a mounting technology that maximizes the performance of LSI devices but for this to be achieved, breakthroughs are needed in the following problem areas:

1. mitigation of differences in the thermal coefficient of expansion (TCE) between the LSI device and the substrate;
2. heat dissipation; and
3. countermeasures for, and control of, noise.

For instance, when a silicon LSI device is mounted, under conditions of actual use, the heat generated will cause warping because of differences in the TCE of the LSI device and the materials surrounding it (such as the substrate,

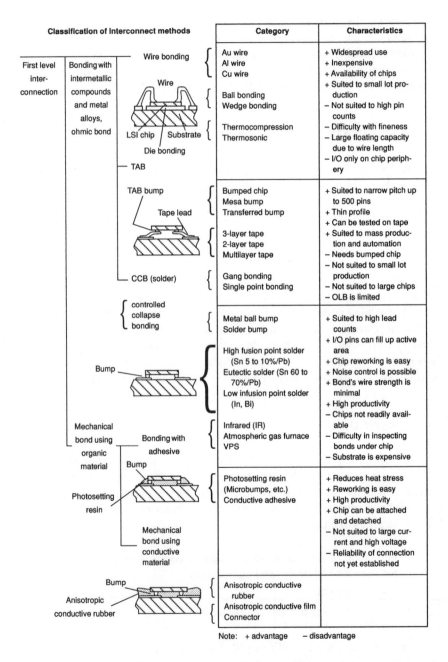

Classification of interconnect methods	Category	Characteristics

First level inter-connection — Bonding with intermetallic compounds and metal alloys, ohmic bond — Wire bonding	Au wire
	Al wire
	Cu wire
		+ Widespread use
		+ Inexpensive
		+ Availability of chips
		+ Suited to small lot pro-
		   duction
		− Not suited to high pin
		   counts
		− Difficulty with fineness
		− Large floating capacity
		   due to wire length
		− I/O only on chip periph-
		   ery

Wire / LSI chip / Substrate / Die bonding	Ball bonding Wedge bonding	
	Thermocompression Thermosonic	

TAB — TAB bump / Tape lead	Bumped chip
	Mesa bump
	Transferred bump
		+ Suited to narrow pitch up
		   to 500 pins
		+ Thin profile
		+ Can be tested on tape
		+ Suited to mass produc-
		   tion and automation
		− Needs bumped chip
		− Not suited to small lot
		   production
		− Not suited to large chips
		− OLB is limited

	3-layer tape 2-layer tape Multilayer tape	
CCB (solder) — controlled collapse bonding	Gang bonding Single point bonding	

Bump	Metal ball bump
	Solder bump
		+ Suited to high lead
		   counts
		+ I/O pins can fill up active
		   area
		+ Chip reworking is easy
		+ Noise control is possible
		+ Bond's wire strength is
		   minimal
		+ High productivity
		− Chips not readily avail-
		   able
		− Difficulty in inspecting
		   bonds under chip
		− Substrate is expensive

	High fusion point solder
	   (Sn 5 to 10%/Pb)
	Eutectic solder (Sn 60 to
	   70%/Pb)
	Low infusion point solder
	   (In, Bi)	

Mechanical bond using organic material — Bonding with adhesive	Infrared (IR) Atmospheric gas furnace VPS	

Bump — Photosetting resin	Photosetting resin
	   (Microbumps, etc.)
	Conductive adhesive
		+ Reduces heat stress
		+ Reworking is easy
		+ High productivity
		+ Chip can be attached
		   and detached
		− Not suited to large cur-
		   rent and high voltage
		− Reliability of connection
		   not yet established

Mechanical bond using conductive material		
Bump — Anisotropic conductive rubber	Anisotropic conductive rubber	
	Anisotropic conductive film Connector	

Note: + advantage   − disadvantage

Fig. 3   Classification and characteristics of first-level mounting methods for LSI devices.

tape, and encapsulating resin), which in turn can destroy the interconnection and cause failure. This problem will become more serious as chips become larger in size and higher in integration level and pin count. Recently introduced silicon-on-silicon packages, which mount silicon LSI chips onto silicon substrates (Fig. 4), are a new attempt to overcome this problem and thoroughly investigate ideal packaging forms.

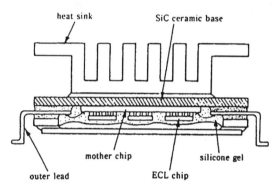

(a) Hitachi microminiature multichip flatpack module

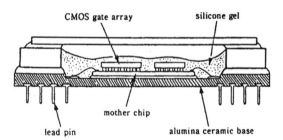

(b) Hitachi microminiature multichip pin-grid-array module

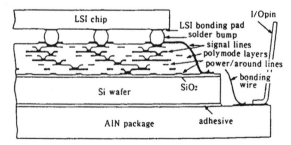

(c) cross-sectional construction of chip-on-wafer technology

Fig. 4   The new silicon-on-silicon package.

REFERENCES

[1] R. Tummala, E. Rymaszewski, *Microelectronics Packaging Handbook*, Van Nostrand Reinhold, pp. 9–33.

[2] G. Ginsberg, "Multichip modules for advanced applications," *Proc. 1990 SMART VI*, pp. 426–427, 1990.

[3] S. Kimijima, "High-density multichip module by chip-on-wafer technology," *Hybrid Circuits*, no. 21, p. 33, January 1990.

Part 2

SMT Equipment

Trends in the Interconnect Equipment Industry in the 1990s

Press Journal Editors

INTRODUCTION

The approach to mounting has changed significantly in the last year or two. Previously, semiconductor suppliers and chip type component suppliers had each devised their own business strategy. Even in the printed circuit board industry, wiring board suppliers and circuit board makers each followed their own course. Thus while extolling the virtues of consensus building, each industry was in fact pursuing its own end. However, the attitudes of these industries have changed with the diffusion of high density mounting with SMT. This is because of the wider selection that system makers have with respect to substrates, components, LSIs, and mounting methods. Thus suppliers can no longer call the plays. What are related industries responding to, and with what technologies, in their product development? Furthermore, a wide range of information is in demand regarding development trends in manufacturing equipment and materials. Based on these considerations, we will report on the trends in the mounting equipment industry for the 1990s (see Fig. 1).

PLACERS

Placers can be broadly classified into chip placers, which feature high speed, and integrated circuit (IC) placers, which handle a variety of components and have high precision.

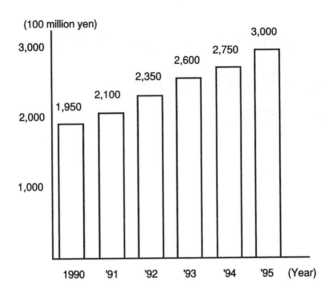

Fig. 1   Mounting equipment market.

Chip Placer

As suppliers have achieved a mounting speed of 0.2 seconds per device, higher speed is being pursued by increasing the number of mounting nozzles. Machines are presently equipped with 40 to 50 nozzles, with some having nearly 100 nozzles, depending on the manufacturer. In terms of component size, all suppliers have an established record with 1608 components, and several have announced machines that can accommodate 1005 components, for which mass production began early in 1991. However, the taping method for 1005 chips has yet to be standardized, and as a result placer suppliers continue to stand on the sidelines. System makers are not entirely satisfied with this latest size reduction. While they want the higher mounting density that smaller components make possible, the smaller size of the capacitors makes them inadequate and actually has the ironic effect of making the 1608 size more efficient for mounting. In any case, the trend in chip component size reductions has stopped at 1005 and composite chip components will be the trend of the future (see Fig. 2).

IC Placer

The main development issue with IC placers is accommodating a 0.3 mm lead pitch. Recognition technology in particular is behind in development. At present, equipment with a positioning accuracy of 30 to 50 μm is available

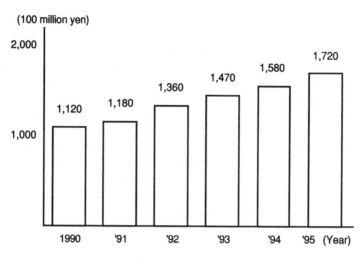

Fig. 2 Mounter market.

(recently, equipment with a 10 μm accuracy was developed). However, on the factory floor the arm cannot stop accurately because of inertia, resulting in positioning error. While the mounting speed of the placers from each of the suppliers is in the 0.6 sec/device range, approximately 2 to 8 seconds is required for lead inspection. With the inevitable trend toward higher pin counts, accuracy will be emphasized over high speed, and the sooner recognition technology is established, the better.

Choice of Placer Depends on Application

When we looked at the placers available on the market, we found that they were all general-purpose placers that accommodate both chip components and ICs. This is a feature peculiar to Japanese industry, and is based on the idea that it is more convenient and cost effective to have one machine doing two different things than to have two dedicated machines. However, stated another way, it can mean that there is no firmly established concept with regard to mounters. For instance, even now no attempt is being made to reduce the setup time. This takes four hours, on average, and can take up to six hours. It is no longer enough to be content with merely being able to place components on the board. While maintaining the present level of performance, it is necessary to pay careful consideration to details such as adhesive pressure. There is a trend away from multipurpose machines and toward specialized machines, and placer suppliers who are slow to adapt will be weeded out.

Bare Chip Mounting

One market segment that has begun expanding rapidly because of the narrower pin pitch accompanying higher pin counts is tape automated bonding (TAB) inner lead bonders (ILB). Performance characteristics shared by equipment suppliers in this market include a bonding accuracy of about 10 µm, 70 mm tape width (some can accommodate 158 mm tape width) and a maximum bonding load of at least 30 kg. These figures are drawn from specification sheets, and in practice the bonding accuracy using good quality tape is about 15 µm, while the bonding load varies with material quality. A pending development problem for every company is the parallelism of the heating tool. Until now, progress on this issue has depended on learning from experience, and while improvements such as the implementation of a micrometer have occurred, automation is still not close at hand. In other words, whichever TAB mounting machine one looks at, a number of problems need solutions. The ILB market is currently dominated by driver IC mounting for liquid crystal displays, while ordinary substrates are using only a few TAB packages per board. However, TAB is the only mounting technology capable of lead pitches narrower than 0.3 mm. Of the numerous mounting technologies that have been introduced, TAB is the only technology that has accumulated 20 years of experience and is being used at the mass production level. If the process technology is established, and if inspection and reliability technologies are soon developed, the market can be expected to surpass the growth predicted in Fig. 5. If we look only at pin count, the use of TAB in pin grid arrays (PGA), bonding begins at pin counts of around 300 and, according to some reports, the pin count could climb to 700 in the next year or so for PGAs at the leading edge. While tape and equipment suppliers will need to accommodate decreasing pad pitch and narrower lead width, each breakthrough will, without fail, cause the TAB market to expand. As for outer lead bonders, because bonding specifications vary with each user, the shipment of standardized bonders is rather limited for each company at the moment. Because most system makers have this equipment manufactured by their subsidiaries, it is difficult to get a grasp of the total market (see Fig. 3).

ISSUES RELATED TO BONDING EQUIPMENT

The era of lead pitches beyond 0.3 mm has been dubbed the solderless era. However, this does not mean that solder will not be used, as soldering equipment is required for mounting. System makers, who have had many years of experience with solder bonding, actually want to use soldering as long as possible. The most urgent issue is to establish the bonding technology for 1005 chip components and 0.3 mm-pitch packages. The bottlenecks to achieving this are the accuracy of sol-

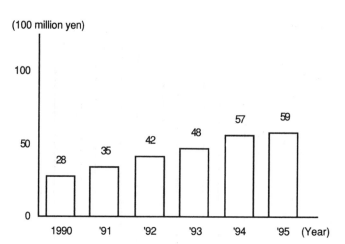

Fig. 3 Bare chip mounting (inner lead bonder) market.

der printers and solder strength reliability after bonding. For example, with regard to 0.3 mm pitch, solder printing precision cleared 0.4 mm only recently and 0.3 mm-pitch is likely to take a while longer. The problem is not in printing the solder for a single component, but with matching the printing with the other mounted components. As for solder strength, because the lead width is only about 0.18 mm, there is roughly enough space for three and a half particles if the solder particle diameter is 50 μm, or six particles if the particle diameter is 30 μm. Furthermore, with a lead interval of only about 0.12 mm, it is extremely difficult to ensure both conductivity and strength while not allowing bridges to form. According to unconfirmed rumors, a package has been developed that has leads coated with insulation film to prevent solder bridging. However, because the part of the leads touching the pads obviously cannot be coated, and because the pitch does not change, it is not clear how bridging is prevented with this method when the solder is squeezed together. Another experimental method to prevent bridging uses a photographic pattern formation method to deposit resist between the leads. Figs. 4 to 6 show the projected outlook for the bonding equipment market.

Hot Air and VPS Methods

Two types of soldering equipment for 1005 chip components and 0.3 mm-pitch packages are hot air and VPS. The hot air method is expected to mature in the next one to two years and experience growth thereafter. An as yet unsolved problem with this method is temperature variation. As the descriptive name states, this method uses only heated air and thus requires a substantial amount of heat. This aspect could be improved by using heat convection. Further, the prob-

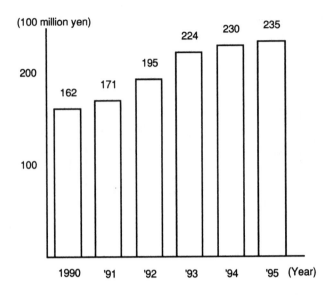

Fig. 4   Solder printing equipment market.

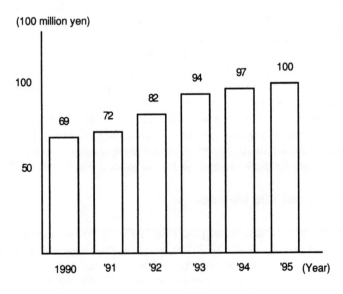

Fig. 5   Adhesive coating equipment (dispenser) market.

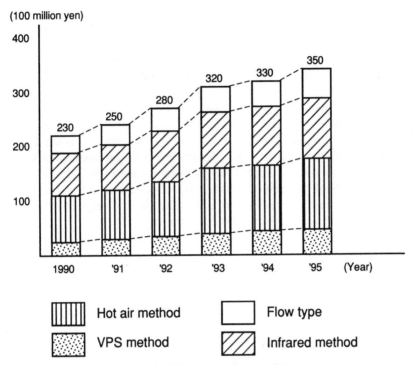

Fig. 6 Soldering equipment market.

lem of air speed cannot be ignored. As pin pitch and chip component electrode spacing become narrower, there is the danger that components may shift unless the air speed is optimized. Meanwhile, the VPS method is also confronted with the issue of temperature variation. In addition, problems with wicking and tombstone phenomena have not been completely solved. While companies are doing their best with regard to preheating, because the cooling equipment for fluorinate recovery reduces the temperature of the preheated substrate, it has been suggested that the reflowed portion is exposed to a sudden temperature increase, resulting in the tombstone effect. The VPS market is expected to reach 1.5 billion yen in 1990 and 2.8 billion yen by 1995. However, if the low temperature (175° C fusion point) soldering equipment already in practical use by certain consumer product makers spreads to system makers, then the VPS market will probably expand significantly and even encroach on the hot air market.

Nitrogen Reflow Method

One of the new areas of activity being watched is nitrogen reflow equipment. The nitrogen reflow atmosphere effectively prevents the oxidation of copper wiring and makes possible the elimination of cleaning after reflow. While the flux basically consists of rosin and an activator, for use in the nitrogen atmosphere it is premised on wax and a weak activator. Because the wax has a fusion point of 100° C, it gassifies under the 230° C of the reflow process. The low-residue weak activator does not need to be cleaned. However, there is a problem with regard to the proper viscosity required of flux. There are also unresolved issues with the equipment, including an equipment size and cost that are two to 2.5 times greater than reflow equipment in general, and the installation of environmental facilities for handling gassified wax. Above all, not only is the domestic price of nitrogen high, but the required purity level calls for an oxygen content in the 10 ppm order, which is beyond the standards of commercially available nitrogen. Regardless of its technical merits, the method is useless if its cost performance is inadequate. This equipment is supported most strongly by kiln makers, who are expected to carry forward its development.

Flow and Infrared Methods

While the above discussion on placers and bonders is already receiving considerable attention, not all mounted components will be replaced by 1005 chip components and 0.3 mm-pitch packages. The mainstream in mounting formats will, above all else, remain a mixed substrate. Breakthroughs continue to be demanded of flow soldering and infrared soldering equipment. In flow-type equipment, warpage associated with increasingly thin multilayer substrates is causing defective solder connections. In the double wave method, the leads are immersed for two to three seconds. Because the point at which the solder is cut differs between the first and second wave, the problem is whether to set the optimal value in the first or second wave. A faulty setting tends to produce a large number of bridges. The infrared reflow method also has a strong appeal. While conceding the high density substrate market to the hot air and VPS methods, this method will continue to secure a sound position in the market because of its low cost and ease of use. One issue with this method is to achieve a good balance between the different heat absorption rates of dark colored and shiny components.

Optical and Laser Methods

Optical and laser soldering methods are not suited to mass production uses but are capable of accurate soldering. For this reason, they have carved a niche in markets where lives are at stake, such as in assembling substrates for automotive and aeronautical applications. They are also useful in equipment for repair work.

CLEANING

Details of the market for cleaning agents and cleaning equipment are unclear. Because of the diversification of cleaning methods, differentiation of solvents and equipment, and unfinished evaluations from users, a total has not yet been calculated.

System makers of consumer products are strongly inclined toward non-cleaning methods. At present, flux can be divided into rosin, nonresidue, and water solvent types. Rosin flux can be further divided into R (rosin + solvent), RMA (rosin + weak activator), and RA (rosin + strong activator). At least 90% of the Japanese market had been using RA rosin flux combined with freon cleaning. Presently, attention is focused on noncleaning methods using RMA flux. Some rosin and activator are left after reflow, as the substrate is covered by the activator, which in turn is covered by the rosin. The idea is that while the activator can absorb humidity, the rosin does not, and so if the entire substrate is coated then there is no need for cleaning. The hardened rosin is extremely stable, and the activator has no harmful effect whatsoever on the substrate. For instance, a printed board exposed to the high humidity in a freezer has been treated with the noncleaning method with a 10 mm-thick glue coating on top and 10 mm underneath for a total thickness of 20 mm. However, not all substrates for industrial use utilize the noncleaning method. Exceptions include computers, special applications for space, and automotive substrates. In dead summer, car temperatures can exceed 100° C. Because rosin has a softening temperature of 80° C, the coating can melt and possibly cause an accident. There is also a limitation in consumer products in the form of in-circuit testing. Because flux is an insulator, the accumulation of any on the test pins could interfere with the test.

Residue-free flux uses a composite resin in place of rosin and has its sales point in not leaving any residue. However, it actually leaves a thin film of activator and is thus weak against humidity. This results in the occurrence of leaks and copper wiring corrosion, as well as poor solderability because of the lack of rosin. The third type of water soluble flux may be soluble in water, but this also means it absorbs humidity. As a result, it raises the same concern as residue-free flux and boosts process management requirements to a new level.

The discussion on cleaning has been limited to flux because cleaning agents and equipment are still undergoing evaluation. Users are less concerned about the cleaning method than about having to wait for the establishment of a water drainage process flow. Electrical makers in general are weak in the area of drainage processes and this leads them to impose demands on plant contractors that sometimes result in problems.

INSPECTION AND RELIABILITY EQUIPMENT

Printed circuit boards are so costly to inspect that they have been referred to as "test hell." In fact, the current state of inspection technology is actually hampering substrate and process technology.

Automated Optical Inspection Equipment

The market for automated optical inspection equipment (AOI) shown in Fig. 7 is for bare boards. Introduced some three to four years ago, their in-line installation has become possible and there are no major problems. Their cost, at around 10 million yen, is reasonable as well. The problems lie with AOI equipment for mounting boards. These machines were in the limelight about two years ago and were introduced into factories, but since then have been put aside to collect dust. A number of solderability problems have arisen, which is associated with the increase in mounting density. AOI inspection can fail, for instance, to

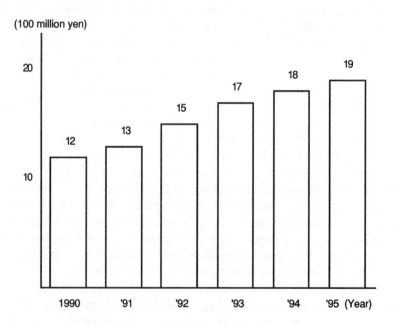

(100 million yen)

Fig. 7   Automated inspection equipment (AOI) market.

detect "tempura" solder defects (where a solder bond looks good on the outside but is hollow on the inside and does not connect the lead and pad). Users demand that the inspection equipment be capable of analyzing solder bonds internally but there is disagreement between equipment suppliers and users over the cost of adding this capability, which has left the market in a depressed state. This spring, trading companies of several suppliers announced inspection equipment capable of solderability analysis, and it remains to be seen if this new movement will invigorate the market.

In-circuit Tester

In-circuit testers vary considerably in price and application, depending on whether they are domestic or imported. The domestic variety costs from 1.5 million to 30 million yen and may go as high as 40 million yen. The test jig costs from 100,000 to 200,000 yen for testing single-sided boards and 500,000 yen for double-sided boards. Their application is limited to checking for defects. Imported equipment costs from 30 million to 120 million yen. The test jig costs between 500,000 to 1.5 million yen for single-sided boards and 3 million yen for double-sided boards. Their application is defect analysis. System makers have improved their production efficiency by installing several domestic in-circuit testers in production lines to check for defects. Defective substrates are then sent to the imported testers for defect analysis. Technologically there is no room left for improvement to this setup. If there were an issue that could be raised, it would be to increase production efficiency to somehow increase throughput. The high density of the mounting prevents proper placement of the probe pins and calls for a breakthrough in the development of new equipment. The market is expected to level off at around 10 billion yen, of which 10% is imports and the rest domestic equipment. In recent years, the market has seen a number of new entrants, but they face an uphill battle against the established firms that hold 70 to 80% of the market (see Fig. 8).

Function Tester

Because function testers test the actual operation of the board assembly, users prefer them to in-circuit testers in the inspection process. However, practical knowledge is still sparse, the program generation is difficult, and the software is not yet mature. There are also problems with the defect rate and analysis time. Because signals are normally input from the outside, the problem is how to accurately locate the defects. In addition, the time required for analysis is from several minutes to several dozen minutes and unless this is reduced, the equipment cannot be used on the line. Figure 9 shows the market trend for logic function testers. The function tester market also has an analog segment, for which the main tech-

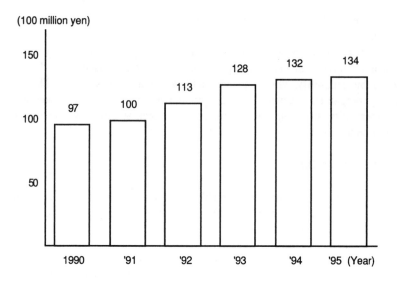

Fig. 8   In-circuit tester market.

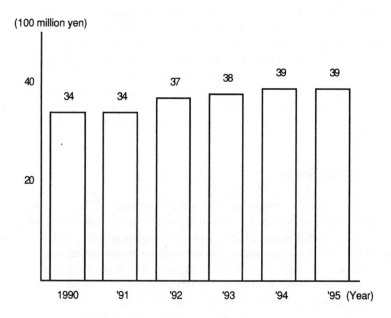

Fig. 9   Function tester market.

nological issue is accommodation of the gigahertz band. Most users are supported by their in-house equipment. For this reason maintenance is a major concern, and market expansion is dependent on the extent to which inspection equipment suppliers can cut into the captive market. The combined logic and analog function tester market is seen as a potential 20 billion yen market, but it remains to be seen how this size can be reached in the next four to five years.

Environmental Testing Equipment

The trend toward thinner, ultra small packages and the diffusion of TAB are creating a demand for technological improvements in environmental testing equipment. Small, ultra thin plastic packages are causing phenomena that were previously unthinkable. When system makers receive a shipment during the hot and humid summer months, the plastic absorbs moisture. Plastic absorbs humidity readily but is difficult to dry out, and drying takes more time than humidifying. This moisture cannot be dried out in an oven and can destroy the package during the reflow process. This problem is not limited to equipment makers alone, as system makers are also presently beginning to reexamine environmental testing standards. In TAB, the problem occurs after inner lead bonding—production efficiency falls drastically between the environmental testing and outer lead bonding. While the nature of this problem cannot be generalized because of the different methods used by system makers, certain system makers are cutting the tape after inner lead bonding and then conducting environmental tests. After the tests, production efficiency falls because the tape is not drawn in. Moreover, some makers conduct their environmental testing with the packages still on tape, but evaluation of this method is difficult. (See Fig. 10.)

CONCLUSION

Trends in the mounting equipment industry in the 1990s have been described above. There are many problems associated with each area, machine, and material. The important point is that the problems in each field are not independent of the other fields. All the fields are interrelated and linked. For instance, the problem of printed board warpage is certain to cause defects in placing and bonding. Unless there are breakthroughs in placing, bonding, cleaning, and inspection technologies, assembly technologies will not make any advances. In this day and age, it is no longer adequate to simply stick components onto boards.

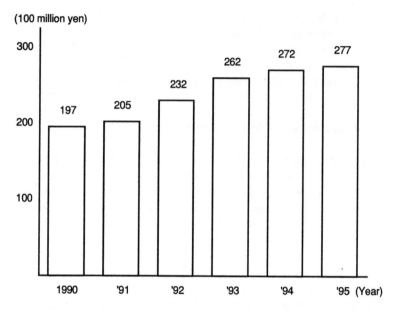

Fig. 10 Environmental test equipment market (for bare boards and mounting substrates including surface mount devices).

Overview of Placement and Bonding Technology for 1005 Components and 0.3 mm-Pitch LSIs: An Equipment Perspective

Kenshuu Oyama

Kyushu Matsushita Electric Co., Ltd.
Production Technology Division

INTERCONNECTION AND ADVANCES IN DEVICE FUNCTIONS

Trends in Electronics Equipment

In recent years, electronics products such as video camcorders, portable phones, personal computers, and electronic notebooks have not only become smaller, but more functional as well. The competition to reduce camcorder size and weight is now well under way, while personal computers have shifted from laptop size to notebook and even to prototype announcements of palm-size computers. Personal computers will soon have built-in portable phones. Figure 1 shows some of these miniaturized electronics products.

Components: Small Size, High Pin Count, and Narrow Pitch

While the demand for smaller electronics products with greater functionality is currently being met with 1608 chip components and quad flat packages

(a) Video camcorder

(b) Notebook computer

(c) Portable telephone

Fig. 1 Examples of miniaturized electronic equipment.

(QFP) with a 0.5 mm lead pitch, the unending pursuit of miniaturization is leading to the use of 1005 chip components and integrated circuit (IC) packages with ever-increasing pin counts.

Although higher pin counts for IC packages would indicate a larger package size, the higher mounting density being required is creating a demand for

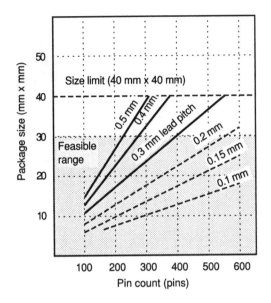

Fig. 2   Lead pitch and package size limits of high-pin-count QFPs.

smaller packages. In soldering as well, large packages are more prone to have unconnected leads due to substrate warpage during reflow. Thus, there is an inevitable tendency toward narrower pitch. In general, assuming the package size limit to be 40 mm^2, the recommended package size for relative ease of handling is below 30 mm^2.

Figure 2 shows that interconnection is practically impossible unless the lead pitch is 0.5 mm for 300 pins, 0.4 mm for 400 pins, and 0.3 mm for 500 pins. These packages will appear in the next two to three years as narrow-pitch, QFP interconnect technology becomes an important issue. Figure 3 shows the trend toward higher pin counts, and narrower lead pitches.

Whether packages have one hundred or several hundred pins, their miniaturization contributes to the trend toward lighter and smaller end products. However, because a gull wing package formed with a conventional lead frame requires that part of the inner lead be imbedded in the mold, a pin pitch reduction below 0.5 mm is not effective for packages with less than 100 pins unless tape automated bonding (TAB) copper foil leads are used. Figure 4 illustrates this type of package.

Next we will investigate the various interconnect methods. The batch soldering method, generally known as mass reflowing, has separate processes for placing and soldering. This is a valuable arrangement because it allows for high-speed placing and the simultaneous bonding of all components. However, when

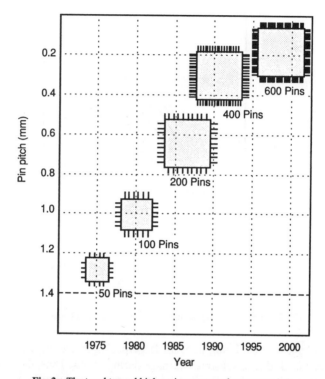

Fig. 3 The trend toward higher pin counts and narrower pitch.

used for narrow-pitch QFP mounting, the method is plagued with such problems
as solder balls and floating leads. Thus, in practice, these packages are soldered
separately. While this practice produces reliable solder joints, the interconnect
cost is inflated by the two- to fivefold increase in time required to interconnect
the various packages. Moreover, because this IC is interconnected along with
conventional components such as resistors, capacitors, and general purpose ICs,
the compatibility of components in the mounting process becomes an important
issue. Stated another way, if conventional components were placed using conventional mounting equipment and narrow-pitch QFPs with specially installed placers, and if all devices could be bonded simultaneously, then existing manufacturing technology could be used with only slight process modifications to minimize
the facilities investment.

Toward Microbonding

As explained earlier, interconnecting ICs with a pitch narrower than the
current minimum of 0.5 mm requires a modification of the package. Extrapolat-

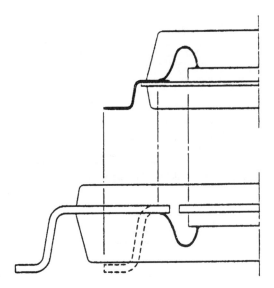

Fig. 4   Reducing package size by using thinner leads.

ing this method into the future leads to the chip on board (COB) method, in which the bare chip is placed directly on the substrate.

Using the conventional reflow process, in which cream solder is printed on the substrate prior to the placement of components, it is quite possible to achieve a 0.4 mm pitch by improvements to the cream solder, printing, and placing. However, while 0.3 mm pitch may be possible at the experimental level, at the practical level there is a great danger of bridging due to the extra solder needed to prevent the QFP leads from floating. Thus, additional refinements are needed for the reflow batch soldering of 0.3 mm-pitch packages. The direction of high density interconnect technology is discussed below.

Figure 5 compares the sizes of different surface mounting methods using the same IC. In general, the material used for IC package leads is a lead frame usually consisting of alloy 42. However, this material will not work with 0.3 mm-pitch packages. One alternative is to use TAB leads.

Looking further, the bonding process can be miniaturized by COB, followed by chip on wafer (COW), and then by wafer scale integration (WSI).

Choosing Between Wire Bonding and TAB

Following is a comparison between wire bonding and TAB for high-pin-count, narrow-pitch LSI packages. With regard to bonding technology, while TAB can bond multiple inner leads, the issue of reliability makes single point bonding highly desirable as the pin count increases. On the other hand, wire

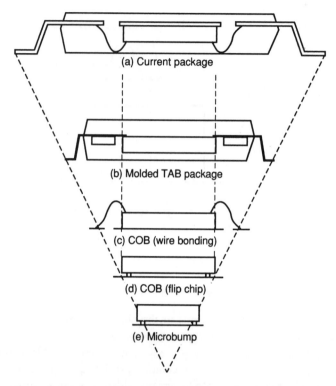

Fig. 5   Comparison of surface areas for different surface mount packages.

bonding has a proven track record with high pin counts and thus offers a sense of security.

As for productivity, the gang bonding capability of TAB is an advantage over the single lead bonding of wire bonding. The two methods diverge when we look at the required loop length for wire bonding. Because the plate thickness of the etching lead frame is around 150 μm, the minimum lead pitch of the inner leads has a process limit of 200 μm. The IC chip, on the other hand, can have a narrower electrode pitch and as the pin count increases, the length of the wire loop must increase as well. For simplification, as Fig. 6 shows, the rectangular arrangement on the left is approximated by the circular layout on the right.

The wire length L is:

$$L = [(200 \times N \div \pi) - (P \times N \div \pi)] \div 2$$

where N is the number of terminals and P is the pad pitch (in millimeters) of the IC. N is:

$$N = [2\pi \div (200 - P)] \times L$$

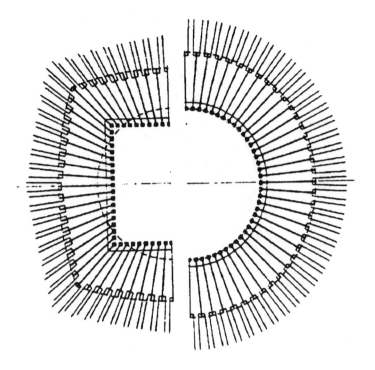

Fig. 6   Views of circular and rectangular wire loop arrangements.

Figure 7 shows N as a function of L.

If the IC pad pitch is 150 µm and the wire loop limit is 3 mm, a maximum of 380 pins can be wire bonded. However, in this case the pad pitch would determine the size of the IC chip. Because the cost of the IC chip is almost entirely determined by its size, a reduction in the pad pitch is highly desirable.

If the IC pads are staggered, bonding is possible down to a pad pitch of around 80 µm. If the loop length is extended to about 4 mm, then the point of divergence between wire bonding and TAB will be around 200 to 250 pins, with packages having pin counts above 300 being relegated to TAB and those with pin counts under 200 to wire bonding.

BONDING QUALITY AND PROCESS TECHNOLOGY

This section examines the process technology for placing and bonding these small electronic components and an analysis of the technical issues.

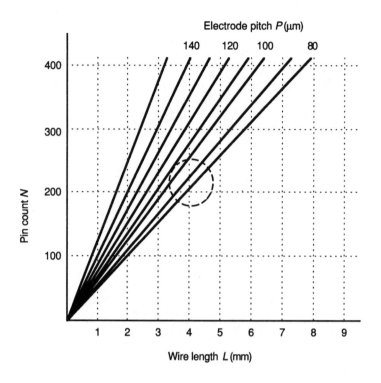

Fig. 7 Pin count, electrode pitch, and wire loop length.

For the reasons listed below, soldering is a widely used interconnect method in electronics equipment and, with some modifications, will clearly continue to play the main role.

1. Solder has a relatively low bonding temperature (under 200° C).
2. Solder has a self-alignment effect when it melts.
3. Solder is viscoelastic at room temperature, absorbing stress caused by vibration and deformation.
4. Soldering is a seasoned technology used since the last century.
5. Soldering is a simple process.

Required Soldering Quality

For the reflow process, the quality requirements for solder joints are:

1. absence of bridges and floating leads when the solder melts,

2. stable amount of solder,

3. good solder wettability,

4. absence of solder balls,

5. easy removal of flux, and

6. firm holding of mounted components.

Figure 8 shows the most serious of soldering defects.

Floating package leads occur to the degree that the leads lack planarity and cannot be eliminated simply by applying the proper amount of solder or preventing the substrate from warping. Thus, the whole issue of the placement of narrow-pitch LSIs must be dealt with by first considering modifications to the package.

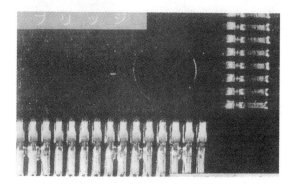

(a) Bridge

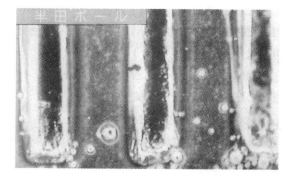

(b) Solder ball

Fig. 8   Examples of the most critical quality problems (continued next page).

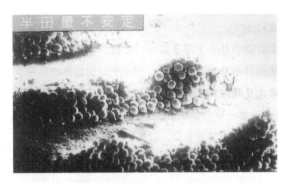

(c) Unstable application of solder

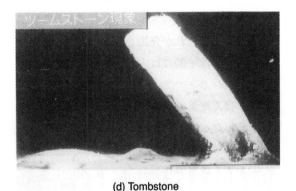

(d) Tombstone

Fig. 8   (continued)

What follows is an analysis of bridges, solder balls, and tombstones and the interdependence of equipment and bonding materials in each process.

Analysis of Factors Causing Bridges

Figure 9 shows the bridge generating mechanism, in which the solder paste slumps and, when the solder is melted, causes a short circuit between adjacent leads. In this case, if the amount of solder is appropriate and the solder has good wettability, the solder will spread to the leads and circuit pattern when melted and not cause bridges. Thus, the amount of solder and its wettability are important factors.

Another cause of bridges is the lack of parallelism in the solder printer such that solder leaks from the gap between the solder screen and substrate to the back side of the solder screen.

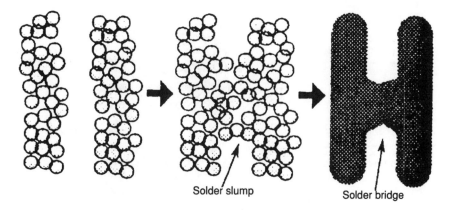

Solder slump

Solder bridge

Fig. 9 The mechanism of solder bridge formation.

Analysis of Factors Causing Solder Balls

The factors causing solder balls are related to those causing bridges in that for some reason the solder paste slumps but then separates from the circuit pattern. However, solder balls can also be caused by the oxidation of the solder particles.

Figure 10 shows the formation of solder balls when the oxidized particles do not melt at the solder fusion point, instead floating in the softened flux and flowing out. Printing paste used to contain irregularly shaped particles that, because of their larger surface area, were more prone to oxidation than spherical particles. Also, because some of the particles were several microns in size, the level of oxidation overall was increased. The occurrence of solder balls also varies with the level of cleaning action of the flux on the oxidized film. Thus, even with some oxidation of the solder particles, a flux with a good cleaning action will eliminate the oxidized film and thereby control the generation of solder balls. Figure 11 shows the interdependent factors causing solder bridges and balls.

Tombstone Generating Mechanism

The tombstone mechanism will be in reference to Fig. 12. Table 1 contains some chip specifications used to calculate the moment strengths in Table 2. The surface tension of the solder is assumed to be 500 dyn/cm, and the tensile angle to be $\theta = 45°$. The results are shown in Fig. 13. The acceptance level used for the solder fillet was 0.5 to 1 T.

It was found that when the solder at the two ends of the chip component melted at different times, the tombstone effect could not be prevented by the

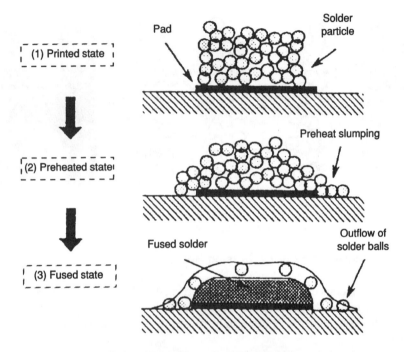

Fig. 10   The mechanism of solder ball formation.

weight moment of the component. To prevent the tombstone, the only alternatives are to rely on the reverse moment of the electrode under the chip component or that of the anchoring strength of the solder paste on the corresponding pads.

The main cause of tombstones, the time lag in the solder fusion at the two ends of the chip component, is another strategy. Figure 14 diagrams the causes of the tombstone phenomenon.

Causes of Defects and Technological Issues

Figure 15, which summarizes the analysis above, shows the complex inter-relationship of causes. For example, bridging can be caused by the printer, placer, reflow equipment, or the bonding material.

1005 CHIP COMPONENT INTERCONNECT TECHNOLOGY

The technical issues mentioned above must be resolved to interconnect fine-featured components. This is particularly true of 1005 chip components, which have

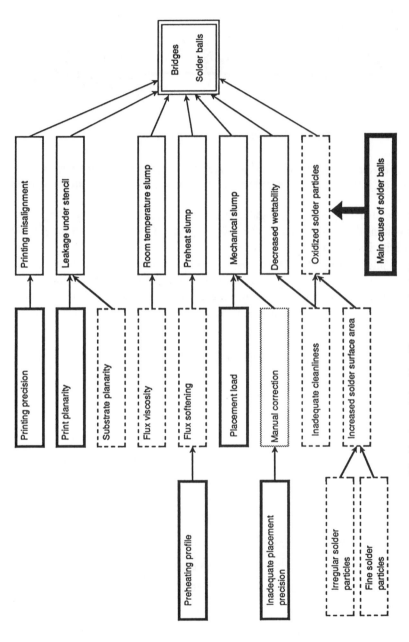

Fig. 11 Interrelationship of factors causing bridges and solder balls.

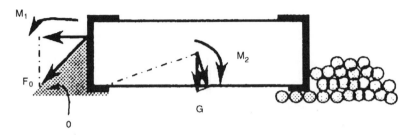

Fig. 12 The mechanism of solder bridge formation.

a surface area of 1.28 to 0.5 mm^2 and are 60% smaller than 1608 chip components. The 1005 fixed resistor weighs 0.7 mg, about 65% less than the 2 mg 1608
version.

Smaller chip size puts tighter restrictions on the settings for the placer.
Fluctuations that were minor for the 1608 chip have a major effect on the placing
rate of the 1005 chip.

While it is important that component suppliers make improvements such as
reducing variations in chip shape and shrinking the gap in the tape cavity, we will
look at how equipment makers can reduce the tombstone effect in 1005 chip
interconnections while maintaining bonding quality and the high speed placing
rate of 0.18 seconds per chip.

Controlling the Pickup Position

TABLE 1 Chip Component Specifications

Chip Resistance	Length (mm)	Width (mm)	Thickness (mm)	G (g)
3216	3.2	1.6	0.6	9.64×10^{-3}
2125	2.0	1.25	0.6	4.92×10^{-3}
1608	1.6	0.8	0.5	2.16×10^{-3}
1005	1.0	0.5	0.35	0.70×10^{-3}

TABLE 2 Moments Working on the Chip Component

Chip resistance	F_0 (gf)	M_1 (gf•cm) = cos $\theta \times T$	M_2 (gf•cm) = $G \times L/2$
3216	0.08	3.39×10^{-3}	1.54×10^{-3}
2125	0.06	2.65×10^{-3}	0.49×10^{-3}
1608	0.04	1.41×10^{-3}	0.17×10^{-3}
1005	0.025	0.62×10^{-3}	0.04×10^{-3}

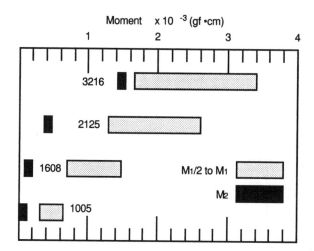

Fig. 13 Solder surface tension and weight moments of chip components.

The small size of the 1005 chip magnifies the effect of the slightest place-ment error. In picking up the chip in particular, misalignment between the center of the nozzle and the center of the chip will cause the nozzle either to miss the chip or to pick it up incorrectly. To achieve a high placement rate, the chip in the tape pocket must be picked up dead center. To meet this requirement, the CM82C-ME high speed placer has a built-in, automated offset function for the pickup position. To reduce damage to the component as well as to accommodate a variety of components, the placer uses the recognition data from a conventional image recognition system to measure the misalignment between the center of the nozzle and the chip, determines the trend, then feeds back the information to automatically correct the pickup position. The correction in the x axis is made to the feeder tape while the correction in the y axis is done by head rotation because the nozzle is located at the periphery of the head. A diagram of this setup is shown in Figure 16.

Controlling the Pickup Gap

Because the thicknesses of the 1005 fixed resistor and capacitor are 0.35 mm and 0.50 mm, respectively, if the down stroke of the pickup motion is set for the capacitor, the fixed resistor is likely to be picked up incorrectly by its side or end because of the gap between the nozzle and resistor. On the other hand, if the placer is adjusted to the thickness of the fixed resistor, the nozzle would land on the capacitor and damage it. To have an optimal pickup gap for both of these components, the up and down motions of the pickup nozzle must be set digitally.

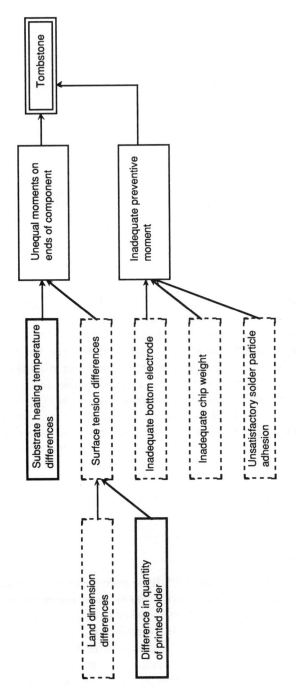

Fig. 14 Interrelationship of factors causing tombstones.

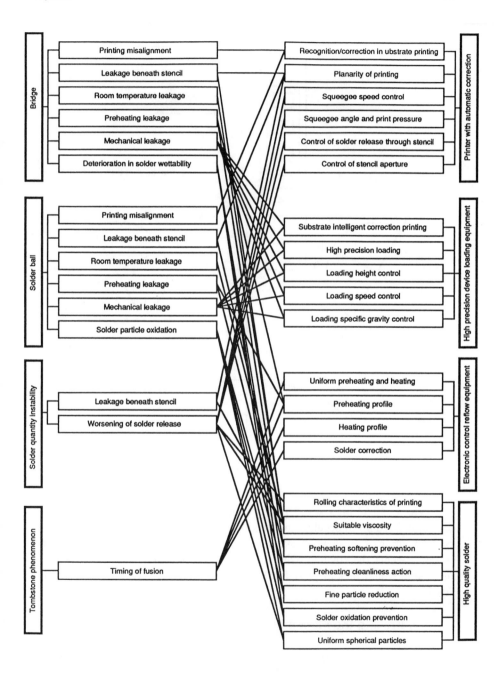

Fig. 15   Types of defect causes and technological issues.

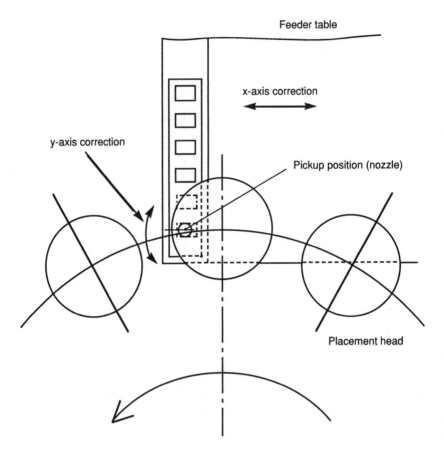

Fig. 16 Conceptual diagram of automatic correction for component-placing equipment.

The CM82C high speed placer employs a cam mechanism with a high degree of freedom in acceleration control. A unique mechanism that allows the lowest position of the down stroke to be set to optimize the pickup gap for different components, thereby improving the pickup rate, has been developed. The nozzle positions and pickup gaps for 1005 resistors and capacitors are shown in Fig. 17.

Controlling the Placement Stroke

The CM82C high speed placer uses digital control not only for the nozzle's pickup stroke but for component placement motion as well. The placement stroke is controlled for component height not only to reduce damage to the component

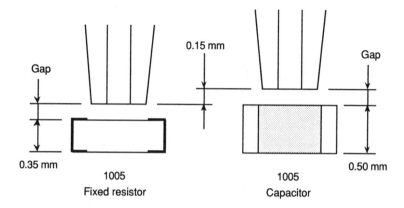

Fig. 17 Optimization of the nozzle gap for pickup.

but to reduce any slumping of the printed solder due to the placement. With 1005 chips in particular, where the pitch between adjacent components is reduced to increase the mounting density, solder bridges between chips must be prevented by controlling not only the placement accuracy but the placement stroke, which prevents solder slumping caused by the placement. The placement strokes for the fixed resistor and electrolytic capacitor are shown in Fig. 18.

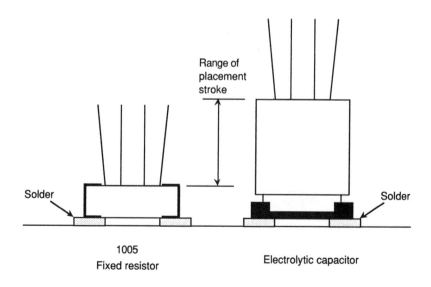

Fig. 18 Optimization of the nozzle stroke range for component pickup.

Chip Recognition Method and Angular Correction

The placement accuracy also affects the solder bonding quality. An important factor for ensuring placement accuracy is chip recognition. To determine the chip's position, the chip, which has been picked up by the suction nozzle, undergoes image recognition at the recognition station, where the angle and deviation of the chip from the center of the nozzle are determined.

The 1005 chip fixed resistor can be distinguished from the capacitor by the sharp corners of the former and rounded corners of the latter. Recognition algorithms for both components have been developed. The recognition images of both are shown in Fig. 19.

Angular correction, using a motor directly connected to the pickup nozzle, is performed relatively slowly during the index time to the placement location. This prevents misalignment due to centrifugal force, even at the high placement speed of 0.18 seconds per component.

Reflow Conditions to Prevent Tombstones

A reflow profile specially designed to prevent tombstones of 1005 chip components is shown in Fig. 20. The point here is to increase the temperature gradually along the temperature gradient to the soak region, from the beginning temperature of 150° C to a temperature close to the solder fusion point (usually 183° C with eutectic solder). The purpose of this procedure is to equalize temperature differences on the substrate by using the substrate's own heat conductivity. In other words, by reducing the substrate's temperature variation as the temperature approaches the solder fusion point, the solder on the pads at both ends of the 1005 component is more likely to melt at the same time.

At this point, it is necessary to consider the selection of a cream solder that is appropriate for soldering with the temperature profile shown in Fig. 20. The considerations are 1) that the solvent dries under the present conditions, and 2)

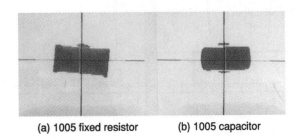

(a) 1005 fixed resistor   (b) 1005 capacitor

Fig. 19   Image recognition of 1005 chip components.

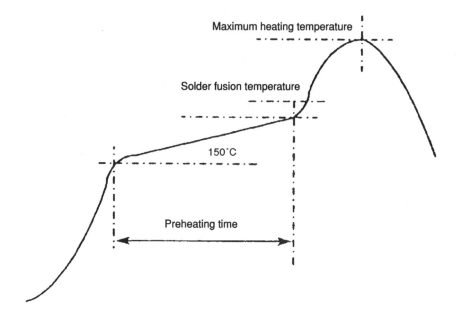

Fig. 20   Reflow profile to prevent tombstones.

that the cream solder does not slump below a temperature of approximately 180° C.

INTERCONNECTION OF 0.3 MM-PITCH LSI PACKAGES

We have already discussed the many advantages of the manufacturing process if the outer leads of narrow-pitch LSI packages could be reflowed simultaneously with other components. Here we will look into outer lead bonding methods for 0.3 mm LSI packages.

Solder Fillets and the Amount of Solder Required

We will calculate the solder fillet shape for QFP leads and the amount of solder required. The amount of solder required to form the fillet in Fig. 21, calculated in terms of the substrate land, is about 40 μm, which is equivalent to 80 μm in terms of the printed film thickness. Because the leads themselves are coated with solder, the required amount of printed solder is actually less. In practice, however, because the QFP leads tend to float, an additional amount of solder is printed for the fillets of these leads.

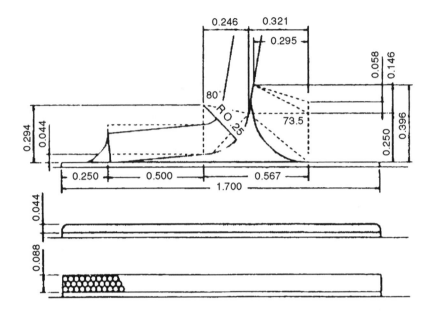

Fig. 21   Solder fillet and the required amount of solder.

Under these circumstances, even if the solder could be printed for a 0.3 mm lead pitch, the solder would slump during placement and greatly increase the occurrence of bridging during soldering. Solder printing measurements for 0.3 mm-pitch QFP leads are shown in Fig. 22.

This amount of solder may not be necessary. If the minimum required amount of solder is precoated onto the QFP leads and the substrate, and if lead floating could somehow be prevented, then it would be possible to use only flux to bond narrow-pitch leads with the conventional mass reflow method.

When copper foil leads are used, only about 10 μm of solder is needed and this can be precoated entirely onto the substrate. However, since copper leads alone will not ensure the mechanical strength required to set a package, the soldered leads can be used only for conductivity. The resin package must be bonded to the substrate with an adhesive for mechanical strength. Figure 23 is a diagram of bonding with precoated surfaces.

Preventing Floating Leads

Conventional QFP package leads are exposed to the danger of bent and floating leads from a wide variety of sources, including testing or burning-in by the semiconductor supplier, packing and shipping, and baking in the assembly process. These factors make it difficult to secure lead measurements directly

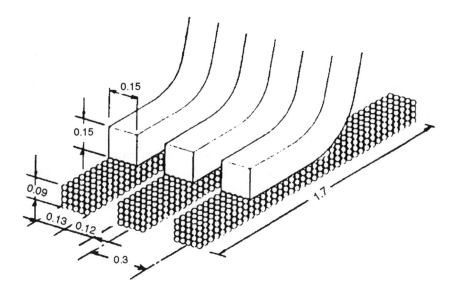

Fig. 22   Solder printing for 0.3 mm-pitch quad flat package.

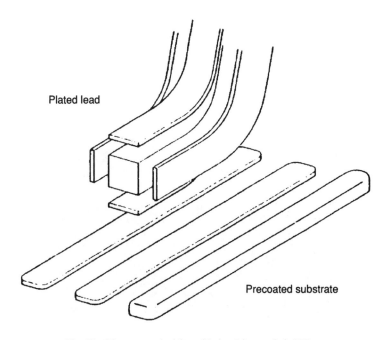

Fig. 23   The new method for soldering 0.3 mm-pitch QFPs.

prior to placement. Thus, in narrow-pitch bonding, the final lead cutting and forming should be performed directly prior to placement. Done this way, the lead formation measurements become the responsibility not of the semiconductor supplier, but of the equipment supplier. One example of this method is National Semiconductor's TapePak®, shown in Fig. 24. Other examples include the flat lead QFP and the molded TAB package shown in Fig. 25. These packages can undergo testing and burn-in as is, with the final lead cutting and forming process performed directly prior to placement.

Copper leads have always been cut and formed directly before placement similar to TAB outer lead bonding. However, the small of amount of solder used necessitates a way of absorbing variations in the leads. This is done by taking advantage of the the adhesion of the molded IC to the substrate for mechanical reinforcement by using the pressure of the leads against the substrate conductors to absorb the variations. This method is illustrated in Fig. 26.

Fig. 24   The TapePak® package.

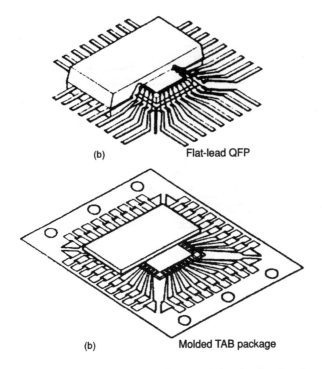

(b)   Flat-lead QFP

(b)   Molded TAB package

Fig. 25 Packages that are excised directly prior to being placed on the substrate.

Managing the Thickness of the Precoated Solder

Conventional solder precoating processes consist of either a plating method or a hot air leveling method. However, there are problems with the plating method itself and with its cost. The hot air leveling method produces an intermetallic compound between the copper and tin that tends to expose the surface and reduce wettability. It thus becomes important to manage the material and amount of solder precoating.

The processed result of a recently announced precoating method is shown in Fig. 27. The method is capable of managing the film thickness to within several microns, is simpler than plating, and does not produce an intermetallic compound. It is indispensable to narrow-pitch bonding.

High Precision Placement

Placement precision is a critical factor in the bonding quality of 0.3 mm-pitch LSI packages. Our multifunction placer used to perform image recognition

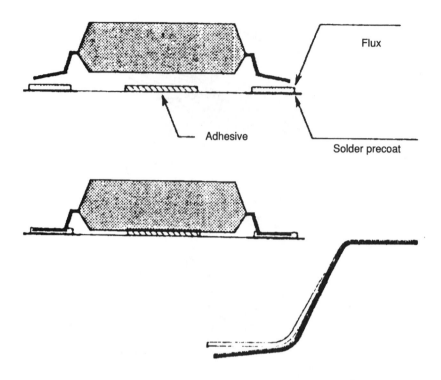

Fig. 26 A method to hold down floating copper foil leads.

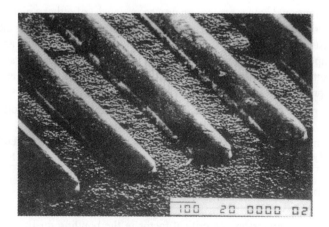

Fig. 27 Surface of newly applied precoat.

of all the leads on a QFP with a CCD camera, then place the QFP in 2.5 seconds with a high degree of precision. However, due to the limited resolution of the CCD camera, the QFP was limited to about 30 mm^2. A separate sensor was needed to detect floating leads. For this reason, we developed a new basic technology that uses laser measurement and accommodates QFPs larger than 40 mm^2. We also made improvements to accommodate 0.3 mm pitch. The principle used to measure all the leads with a laser is shown in Fig. 28 and an example of output waveforms is shown in Fig. 29.

Detection of Bent and Floating Leads

As the lead pitch of QFPs decrease, minute amounts of lead bending and floating tend to have a larger effect in causing defective solder bonds and bridging. Thus, it is important that leads be inspected for any bending or floating prior to placement. The laser measurement method can do just this. Because unfit QFPs can be excluded after lead inspection, the bonding yield on the printed wiring board can be greatly increased.

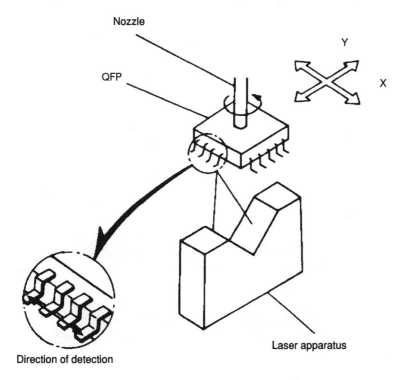

Fig. 28   QFP lead measurement using a laser.

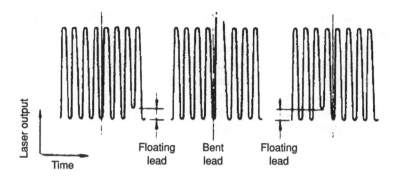

Fig. 29 Laser output waveform and the detection of pitch and floating leads.

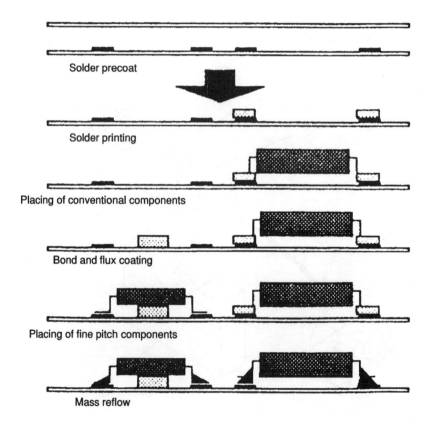

Fig. 30 Mass reflow of different package types.

Diagram of Interconnect Method

Figure 30 is a diagram of a reflow process in which narrow-pitch packages are mounted simultaneously with conventional components.

FUTURE TRENDS

From Molded Packages to Bare Chips

While the trend toward thinner, higher density packaging can easily be extrapolated to the mounting of bare IC chips directly onto the substrate, there are a number of issues to be resolved before this becomes practical.

First is the issue of the reliability of the IC chip. Whereas testing and burn-in can be performed on a molded IC, a bare chip can be tested only after being mounted onto the substrate. Unless the technology is developed to determine whether defects are caused by the IC manufacturing process or the interconnect process, bare chip mounting cannot be adopted. Also, while molded ICs can be handled relatively easily, working with bare chips requires a managed clean environment to prevent corrosion and maintain the necessary cleanness for bonding. Furthermore, to pursue thinner, higher density packaging, repair and product quality issues need to be addressed.

Despite the obstacles to bare chip mounting, it is nonetheless indispensable in pursuing high density mounting. In general, digital ICs, which are relatively easy to test, will evolve toward bare chip mounting while analog ICs, which require testing and classification, will remain in molded packages and achieve higher packaging densities by reductions in lead pitch.

Flip Chip Mounting

Following is a summary of flip chip mounting, a bare chip method in which the leads are bonded simultaneously. Among the ways to interconnect individual chips to a substrate, this is the most representative of thinner packaging methods.

Figure 31 shows a flip chip method using solder bump bonding. The method is widely used in applications ranging from mainframe computers to mobile equipment. Three layers of barrier metals protect the aluminum pads of the IC from the solder, which improves the bonding characteristics but increases the cost.

To reduce the cost of bump formation, the method shown in Fig. 32 uses stud bumps formed by a wire bonder. The bumps are gold and a silver paste is used in the bonding.

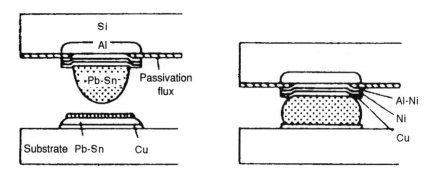

Fig. 31   Flip chip method with solder bumps.

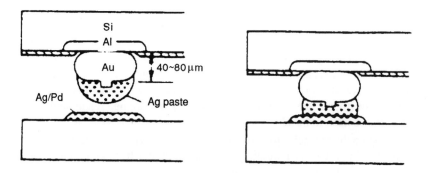

Fig. 32   Stud bump method with silver paste.

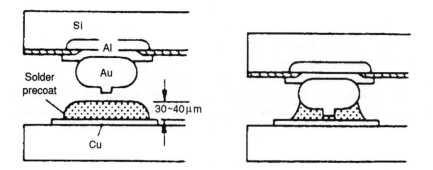

Fig. 33   Stud bump method with solder.

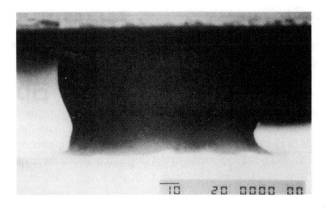

Fig. 34   Reflowed solder joint.

Figure 33 shows a method using the same bumps and a solder bond. The solder is coated beforehand at a thickness of 33 to 40 μm and the bonding is performed by reflow. While the aluminum pads on the IC are protected by a barrier metal, the method is relatively inexpensive. Furthermore, the IC can be reflowed simultaneously with ordinary chip components. Although issues remain to be solved, such as verification of the bond strength using gold diffusion, this method definitely warrants further investigation. A photograph of a bond is shown in Fig. 34.

Reducing the bump pitch would enable the chip size to be reduced as well, leading to reductions in cost. Microbump bonding is being focused on as an interconnect method that will achieve these objectives. A diagram of this method is shown in Fig. 35.

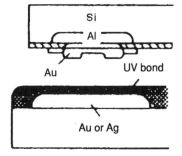
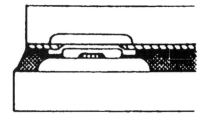

Fig. 35   Microbump method.

Prospects

The above discussion dealt with the placing and bonding of 1005 chip components and 0.3 mm LSI packages and directions in high density packaging. However, these methods are by no means fixed and will continue to evolve, guided by market demand.

Indispensable to the development of these interconnect methods is cooperation in the areas of components, materials, and equipment and the adoption of these methods in electronics equipment. As an equipment supplier, we will probe into these methods and actively seek to develop and improve these methods.

High Reliability Soldering Technology by Hot Air Reflow

Takafumi Yoneyama

Koki Company Ltd.

INTRODUCTION

Spurred by demands from the electronic equipment market, new surface mount devices (SMD) have been developed to achieve greater miniaturization, lower costs, and higher functionality. In turn, a diverse surface mount technology (SMT) has been devised to cope with mounting these devices. A large part of this technology deals with reflow equipment.

In the past, placement equipment has played the principal role, with reflow equipment considered a mere supplement to the production line. Some placement equipment manufacturers have gone so far as to regard reflow equipment as a "giveaway" with the production line. However, reflow soldering technology has grown more complex with the rapid development of SMDs and a greater variety of the boards (e.g., multilayer, flexible, etc.) on which they are placed. No longer can the role of reflow equipment be ignored. In addition, reflow equipment has recently gained the task of soldering discrete components, making reflow an extremely important process.

Reflow equipment employs a variety of heating methods. These include 1) infrared, 2) vapor phase soldering (VPS), 3) hot air, 4) laser, 5) hot plate, and 6) xenon lamp methods. Generally, one of infrared, vapor phase soldering, or hot air is chosen based on productivity factors. Even within these, hot air reflow has gained wide use as an economical method that meets technical requirements.

CHARACTERISTICS OF HOT AIR REFLOW

In hot air reflow, temperature-controlled air is circulated by a fan within the oven. A board is transported through the oven and is heated along the way by convective heat transfer. Hot air is circulated by blowing hot air from a fan located above, or by pulling hot air with a fan located below (see Fig. 1).

Hot air reflow possesses the following merits:

1. Convective heat transfer allows uniform heating. Each object that receives heat has its own thermal absorption coefficient (due to color selectivity) and heats differently under radiant heat, thus increasing the variations in temperature. Nearly all components can now be supplied in surface mount form. This results in boards mounted with many shapes and sizes of components—from big to small, short to tall. Coupled with temperature variations due to differences in each SMD's thermal capacity, the characteristics of radiant heat make uniformly heating the assembly very difficult. Hot air reflow can apply heat uniformly because color selectivity plays no part in convective heating.

2. Shadowed areas are heated efficiently with circulated air. SMDs are designed to be efficiently mounted on a circuit board. Many of these components are fairly difficult to solder. For example, it is particularly difficult to raise the temperature around large-package plastic-leaded chip carriers, filters, and the lead areas of densely packed aluminum electrolyte condensers, making it necessary to apply heat directly to obtain good soldering. The hot air circulated with hot air reflow reaches tight or shaded places, directly heating the subject areas to enable soldering of high-density boards.

3. Temperature is easily controlled, enabling uniform heat. The temperature setting on hot air reflow equipment is nearly the same as the target board temperature. This allows the temperature setting to be easily determined and makes the temperature extremely simple to control. Moreover, while the temperature of components having a small thermal capacity rises easily, it will not rise beyond the temperature of the heat medium itself, the hot air. If there are components of large thermal capacity that do not reach temperature easily and a temperature difference occurs among these and smaller thermal capacity components, small and large components along with the board can be heated to a uniform temperature by lengthening the time spent in the oven.

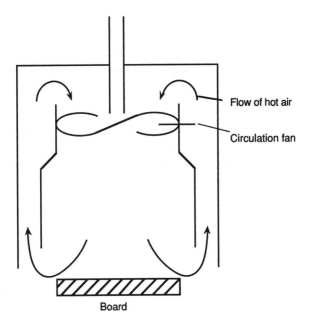

Method of blowing air from above

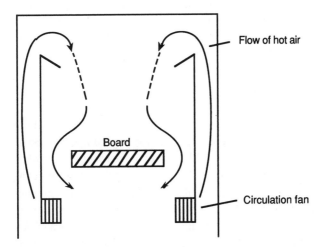

Method of pulling air from below

Fig. 1   Hot air circulation method.

4. Hot air temperature is relatively low, eliminating concerns of heat damage to the board and components. As stated earlier, the hot air temperature setting is very close to the target temperature. In addition, it is a relatively low temperature compared with the heat of an infrared oven; a board left untransported or dropped in an infrared oven burns up. There is no need to worry about such heat damage with a hot air reflow oven.

5. Response time to temperature changes is quick. Quick response time is not a strong merit under normal operating conditions because large changes in the setting temperature are not needed, even with different board types. Nevertheless, there are cases when the reflow oven is switched over to be used for curing small chips, when fine temperature control is done with an automatic changeover function, or when large changes in the temperature setting are made for some reason. Also, when work is finished, a short oven cooling time is desirable. Considering these issues, a quick response time with respect to temperature changes becomes important.

REFLOW OVEN TRENDS

This discussion of hot air reflow equipment begins with an examination of the trends of reflow equipment in typical use, comparing hot air with equipment employing infrared and vapor phase soldering methods. Of course, differences in temperature profiles measured with the same board can be clearly seen due to the differences in the heating method (see Fig. 2). Temperature profile requirements are diverse and complex, but with the results of many evaluations, hot air reflow was judged to be the most suitable.

Because of the weakness inherent in radiant heat, temperature variations among different-sized components, and varying component densities, current infrared reflow technology is unable to satisfy the requirements of new and complex SMT. VPS is superior for uniformly heating the board and components, but with problems of wicking and tombstoning, coupled with high equipment costs and high operation costs (from consumable inactive solvent), it must be reconsidered. Although hot air reflow was initially overlooked because of board oxidation problems, the industrial electronics industry has judged hot air reflow less problematic at current levels of oxidation based on results of consumer electronics applications. Hot air reflow equipment is now gradually replacing VPS. Even in overseas markets, where infrared equipment has been the mainstream, the use and examination of hot air reflow is growing.

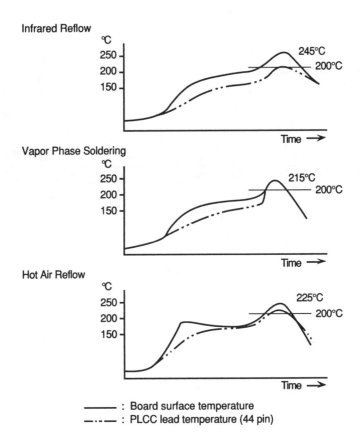

Fig. 2 Temperature profiles of each heating method.

HOT AIR REFLOW OVEN DBUARC-250

The capabilities of hot air reflow ovens naturally make full use of the merits of the hot air method. The operation of the oven must be easy to handle. Figure 3 shows the configuration of the hot air reflow oven DBUARC-250.

Important factors that influence the performance of the hot air reflow oven are the adequate control of board temperature and the air and volume (including speed and flow), as well as the ability to adjust transport speed.

As a means to precisely control the temperature of the hot air, the temperature of the air is measured thermoelectrically, fed back to a thermoregulator, then finely adjusted by PID control.

To ensure adequate heat transfer, a fine heater with a large surface area is used. The oven also has seven sets of temperature settings stored in memory that

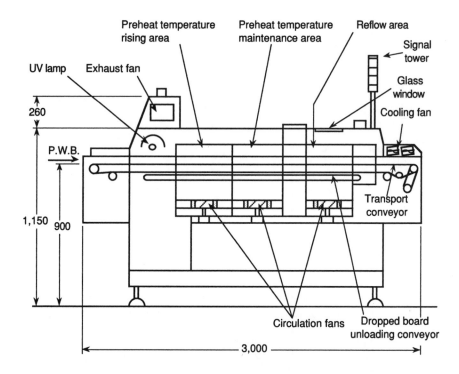

Fig. 3   Configuration of DBUARC-250. Dimensions are in millimeters.

can be chosen by a selector switch so that the oven can be readily used for reflow or curing.

Control of air volume is vital to maintaining stable heat. For uniform heating in particular, there must be a stable hot air volume irrespective of board size or shape, with no variation in the amount applied to the board. This oven generates a consistent heat by controlling and rectifying the flow of hot air with special filters and nozzles.

Even with the temperature setting unchanged, any desirable temperature profile can be obtained by changing the board transport speed through the oven to adjust the temperature slope and heating time of the board. Conversely, when the transport speed differs, the temperature profile may change even if the temperature setting remains the same. For the same speed to be set by anyone, analog speed displays that easily produce individual differences are not suitable. For this reason, the oven is equipped with a digital display to accurately show conveyor speed.

In addition to these basic functions (see Table 1) the DBUARC-250 has the following features:

- Revolving rollers provided as standard equipment allow small boards to smoothly connect with preceding and subsequent line processes.

- An observation window in the reflow area makes it possible to watch the reflow soldering in real time.

- Heaters are structured in blocks that can be easily pulled out, making maintenance work easy. Also, the top of the oven can be fully opened and the conveyor readily reached.

An RS-232C interface to support computer control and automatic changeover is an optional function (see Fig. 4).

TABLE 1   DBUARC-250 Basic Specifications

Handling capability	
Size (mm)	$50^W \times 80^L - 250^W \times 330^L$
Thickness (mm)	0.6–1.6
Height of mounted parts (mm)	25
Board transport speed (mm/min.)	600–1,200
Standard transport speed (mm/min.)	800
Board drop conveyor	Net type (manual)
Transport conveyor	With chain attachment
Option	Personal computer interface
Configuration	
UV area	UV lamp (80 W/cm) 2.8 kW × 1 pc
PH1	Fan heater 0.7 kW × 8 pcs
PH1 sub heater	Infrared panel heater 1.0 kW × 1 pc
PH2	Fan heater 0.7 kW × 4 pcs
Reflow	Fan heater 0.7 kW × 8 pcs
Reflow sub heater	Infrared panel heater 1.0 kW × 1 pc
Cooling area	Propeller fan 0.01 kW × 4 pcs
Painted color	Upper portion: L2-309 Lower portion: L15-846
External dimensions (mm)	$3,000^L \times 1,060^W \times 1,350^H$
Weight (kg)	950
Total power source (kW) (3-phase, 200 V, 50/60 Hz)	21

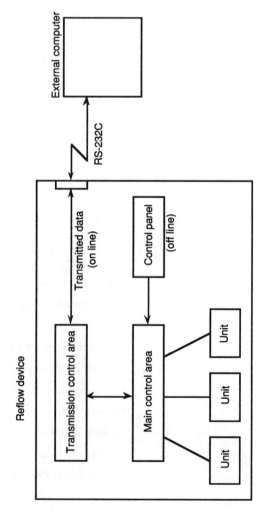

Fig. 4 Overview of computerized reflow device.

REQUIREMENTS FOR REFLOW EQUIPMENT

Functional requirements for reflow equipment have changed and become more multifarious as surface mount technology has been widely introduced and experience has increased. Transitions have been made in transport from net conveyors appropriate for lightweight high-mix manufacturing to chain conveyors that are well suited for double-sided boards. Boards now range from thin and small (glass epoxy with a thickness of 0.1 mm) to thick and large. Components are now placed within 2.5 mm of the board's edge and temperature profile requirements are moving from uniformly heating the entire board to creating a temperature difference between the topside and underside of the board. Thus far we have supplied a hot air reflow oven that meets these requirements, but in the future even more complex and diverse requirements must be supported.

Part 3

Developments in Solder Technology

0.3-mm Pitch LSI Solder Paste Printing Technology

Haruo Mishina
Hiroshi Okada

Hitachi Techno Engineering Co., Ltd.

INTRODUCTION

In recent years demand for smaller, more functional electronic equipment has pushed assembly density higher and higher. To attain higher density, surface mount technology has been introduced. The parts mounted on these assemblies also have become smaller and denser. Large scale integration (LSI) packages, as an example exhibiting these trends [1], show that for quad flat packages (QFPs), which lend themselves to higher densities, the lead pitch has become finer while the lead count has increased. Presently, 0.65-mm lead pitch parts are mainstream [2], with a gradual increase in the use of 0.5-mm lead pitch. Further, the use of 0.4- to 0.3-mm lead pitches has begun to be considered. As a result, establishing highly reliable mounting techniques for fine-pitch LSI packages is in high demand. To bond electronic parts to the board, soldering—which has many strong points—will continue to be employed in the future. Because printing solder paste is the first step in reflow soldering, this is the technological task that must be resolved first. However, it is yet unclear just how far this can be improved in support of fine lead pitches. The print quality of solder paste is determined by many intricately related factors, such as the stencil, squeegee, print conditions, and the solder paste itself, so it is vital to grasp properly the effects of these factors and select suitable conditions. To clarify the technological tasks before us, this paper investigates experimentally the relation solder paste, stencil, and print conditions have in printing solder paste for a 0.3-mm lead pitch QFP.

SOLDER PASTE PRINT QUALITY

Examining Solder Paste

The stencil and groove dimensions used in examining print quality are noted in Table 1. Three pattern groove widths supporting lead pitches of 0.4, 0.5, and 0.6 mm, and three stencil thicknesses supporting lead pitches of 0.33, 0.67, and 1.0 mm were selected. Copper was used as the stencil's core material with nickel-plated surfaces. Because of its availability, SUS was used for the 0.05 mm thick stencil. A glass epoxy resin, copper-clad laminate with no formed pattern

TABLE 1   Stencil

Stencil number	Groove width (mm)	Groove length (mm)	Thickness (mm)	Material
S-1	0.12	1.2	0.15	Cu-Ni
S-2	0.12	1.2	0.15	Cu-Ni
S-3	0.18	1.2	0.15	Cu-Ni
S-4	0.15	1.2	0.10	Cu-Ni
S-5	0.15	1.2	0.05	SUS

TABLE 2   Solder Paste

Solder paste	Standard viscosity (Pa·s)	Thixotropic index	Particle diameter (μm)	Flux content (%)	Flux type
P-1	282.0	0.452	25≈45	8	RMA
P-2	258.0	0.398	≤45	10	RMA
P-3	300.0	0.55	20≈40	10	RA
P-4	290.0	0.488	10≈30	9	RA
P-5	185.0	0.543	≤25	10	RMA

was used as the subject board in order to eliminate effects of pad-to-stencil mis-alignment. The dimensions of the board were 150 × 150 mm with a thickness of 1.5 mm.

Table 2 notes the properties of the solder paste used. Viscosity was measured at 20° C ambient temperature using a viscometer manufactured by Brook-field. The value under a shear rate of 61/S was taken as the standard viscosity and the thixotropic index was derived from the viscosity grade at shear rate. The solder particles were spherical, which gives good print quality with fine-pitch leads.

The solder paste's particle diameter used in P-4 and P-5 was smaller than that used in P-1 to P-3, and the flux was improved. Figure 1 shows representative solder particle shapes.

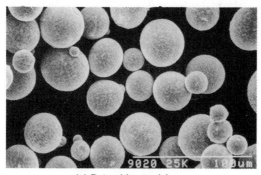

(a) P-1 solder particles

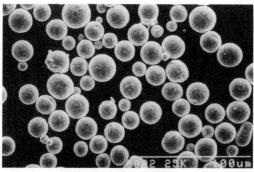

(b) P-4 solder particles

Fig. 1   Solder particle shapes.

Figure 2 shows the print quality of each solder paste in relation to squeegee pressure and stencil-to-board gap when using a 0.3-mm lead pitch pattern and a groove width of 0.15 mm. The squeegee was a flat blade shape made of urethane rubber. The squeegee speed was 10 mm/s.

By observing with a microscope, we evaluated patterns without print defects (such as bleeding or smears) as good (o), those without defects but showing slightly uneven deposition as marginal (Δ), and those with defects as bad (x).

A good print pattern could not be obtained with P-1 and P-3 solder pastes even though they have shown good print quality down to 0.4-mm pitch patterns

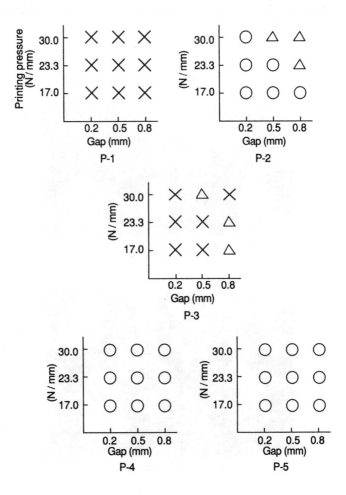

Fig. 2 Solder paste printing characteristics (trench width 0.15 mm).

elsewhere [3]. Good print quality was obtainable with the small thixotropic index and viscosity of P-2 solder paste under some print conditions. In comparison, small particle P-4 and P-5 achieved good print quality under a wide range of print conditions. The conditions that gave good print quality are close to contact printing, thus enabling high accuracy printing with little deflection of the stencil.

Figure 5 shows an example of a good print pattern. P-4 was used as the solder paste with a squeegee pressure of 17 N/mm and a gap of 0.2 mm. In this way we found that the solder paste plays an important role in the print quality.

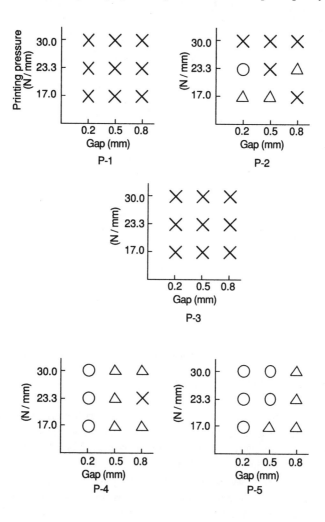

Fig. 3 Solder paste printing characteristics (trench width 0.15 mm).

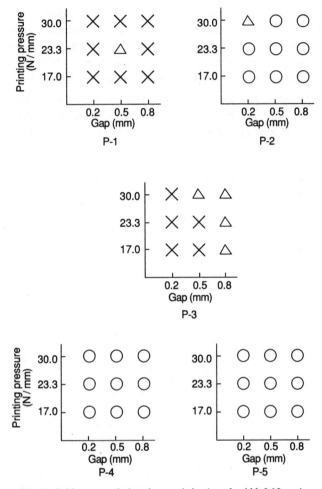

Fig. 4   Solder paste printing characteristics (trench width 0.18 mm).

Examining Stencil Thickness

As lead pitches become finer, the print pattern's comparative height and thickness becomes greater if the stencil thickness remains the same. This leads to the print pattern losing its shape when parts are placed or when prebaked, which ultimately causes solder balls and bridges.

Because of this, we examined the solder paste print quality with different stencil thicknesses. Figure 6 shows the print quality of P-5 solder paste with two stencil groove widths when changing the stencil thickness among 0.15, 0.10, and 0.05 mm. Looking at the range in which good prints are obtained shows that for

⇐ Print direction

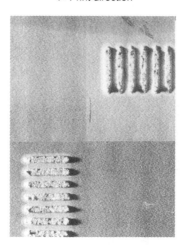

Fig. 5   Example of a good print pattern.

0.15-mm groove width stencils, the good print range gradually narrows as the stencil thickness falls below 0.15 mm. For 0.12-mm groove width stencils, the range of good prints is the widest with a 0.1-mm-thick stencil. In the case of the 0.05-mm-thick stencil with 0.15-mm groove widths, because the stencil is thin, the number of solder particles collected in the stencil is small and the seal of the stencil is reduced with the combined pulling by the squeegee and the easy stencil deflection caused by the squeegee pressure. Therefore, bleeds and smears occur together. On the other hand, with the 0.05-mm-thick stencil, the stencil seal is improved with the longer distance between grooves on the 0.12-mm groove widths, compared with the 0.18-mm groove widths. However, because the groove widths are narrower and the solder paste has difficulty penetrating the stencil, the squeegee pressure must be high and the stencil-to-board gap large to obtain good print quality. When the gap is large, the stencil deflection is great near each end in the direction of squeegee movement when the stencil has grooves covering its full face. In this case, caution is required because print quality can become poor.

CONSECUTIVE PRINTS

At the actual printing process it is important to get a large number of consecutive, good-quality prints without defects. According to our test results, groove widths of 0.15 mm and 0.18 mm got only 1 to 2 boards, and 0.12-mm groove widths consecutively produced only 1 board with a good print. Figures 7 and 8 show the

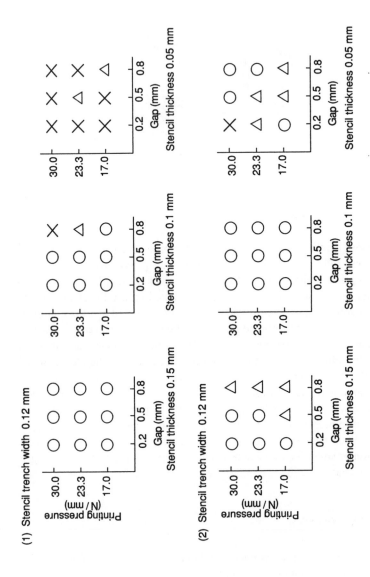

Fig. 6 Printing characteristics of various stencil thicknesses and trench widths (P-5 solder paste).

⇐ Print direction Print direction ⇒

(a) Print pattern (b) Underside of stencil

Fig. 7 Print pattern and underside of stencil (groove width of 0.15 mm).

⇐ Print direction Print direction ⇒

(a) Print pattern (b) Underside of stencil

Fig. 8 Print pattern and underside of stencil (groove width of 0.15 mm).

solder stuck on the stencil surface and print pattern in respect to the groove width when print defects occurred. The stencil thickness was 0.15 mm and the solder paste used was P-4.

With the 0.12-mm groove width stencil, solder adhered to the underside of the stencil between and along the groove edges for grooves lying parallel to the squeegee movement. For grooves lying perpendicular to the squeegee movement, solder paste adhered fully to the inside of the groove. The results of this are solder smears and insufficient solder with grooves lying parallel to, and insufficient solder for grooves lying perpendicular to, squeegee movement. In contrast, solder adhered between and along all groove edges of the 0.15-mm groove width stencil, causing both smears and insufficient solder for all grooves.

If the solder does not adhere to the groove edges, flux bleeding remains when the underside of the stencil is cleaned with a cloth, but the print pattern is restored to nearly its original state. However, solder paste adhering to the inside of the grooves cannot be adequately eliminated by cleaning with a cloth and solder defects will result. A new cleaning method is needed.

CONCLUSION

Taking a 0.3-mm lead pitch QFP as the subject, we examined the print quality when solder paste, stencil, and print conditions are changed. The results show that with the right combination, 0.3-mm pitch patterns can be printed without defects. However, the number of consecutive prints without defects is extremely low— just 1 to 2 boards. To increase number of consecutive quality prints, further examination of the stencil shapes and solder paste properties and development of new stencil cleaning methods are required. Furthermore, when QFPs with differing lead pitches are mixed, a need arises to adjust the solder volume within the same stencil. The amount of solder depends on the QFP lead accuracy, so improvements in dimensional accuracy are important as well.

REFERENCES

[1] Tanimoto: *Development Trends in Advanced Surface Mount LSI Packages and Interconnect Technology Symposium,* Technology Information Center, pp. 1–26, February 1988.

[2] Ohtsuka, Suzuki, Kimoto: "Trends in high pin count QFP packaging," *Semiconductor News,* pp. 15–23, October 1989.

[3] H. Mishina, H. Okada, S. Yawata: "Printing quality of solder paste for IC packages with fine pitch leads," *IMC 1990,* pp. 479–484, June 1990.

Flat Package Soldering Technology

Kazumichi Machida
Yasuyuki Nakaoka

Mitsubishi Electric Corp
Production Technology Research Laboratory

INTRODUCTION

Surface mount boards mounted with large-scale integration (LSI) electronic components are forming the leading-edge product hub about which today's electronic equipment is developed. On a typical printed circuit board, several hundred components connected through several thousand solder joints are mounted en mass. To obtain greater compactness and higher functionality in the product, the design density is increasing at an accelerating rate. Figure 1 illustrates the transitions in mounting methods to support these high-density developments. Figure 2 depicts representative mounting methods.

In the early periods of mount technology, the mainstream method involved inserting component leads into through-holes in the board. Later, as components grew smaller, surface mount became the commonplace method. Now, with boards requiring even higher densities, a bare chip mounting method in which a semiconductor chip is mounted directly to the board is beginning to reach the level of practical use. In the near future, flexible connection of bare chips in line on the board with a focusing deposition beam will likely be practical. Despite these developments, we predict that soldering, with its numerous strong points, will remain a mainstream mounting method.

Against this backdrop, solder connections that join components to the board most become ever finer. In this article, we will focus on the current mainstream soldering processes for attaching fine-pitch lead packages within surface mount applications.

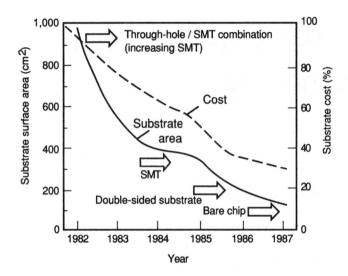

Fig. 1 Transitions in mounting methods and high density developments.

REFLOW SOLDERING

Figure 3 shows a typical method of attaching components to surface mount boards. Here solder paste is printed onto the board using a stencil. Components are then placed very precisely on the board, taking advantage of the solder viscosity to hold the components in place. Next, the board is soldered en mass by a reflow heat source. As a reflow heating method, mass reflow, which shows superior productivity, is used most widely in production lines. But where special consideration must be given to the effects of heat on the components themselves, localized heating is employed. This article discusses the use of infrared, vapor phase soldering, and hot air for mass reflow, and laser or optical beam soldering for localized reflow.

The principles of each type of reflow device are given in Fig. 4. Furthermore, the temperature profile of the board surface is shown in Fig. 5 for each of the mass reflow methods.

Infrared Reflow

Infrared reflow uses the radiated heat of the infrared beam to apply heat to the board and is the most common reflow method. The rate of heat absorption differs according to the subject materials, the color of the board, and the wavelength of the infrared light. Furthermore, without due consideration of these and other factors when designing the board layout, minuscule chips can be overheated

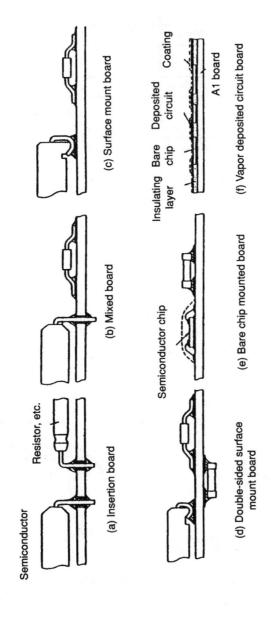

Fig. 2 Representative mounting methods.

Semiconductor

Resistor, etc.

(a) Insertion board

(b) Mixed board

(c) Surface mount board

Semiconductor chip

(d) Double-sided surface mount board

(e) Bare chip mounted board

Insulating layer　Bare chip　Deposited circuit　Coating

A1 board

(f) Vapor deposited circuit board

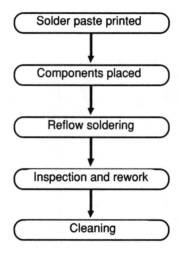

Fig. 3   Configuration of a surface mount line.

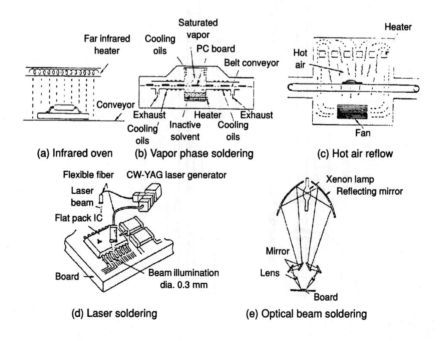

Fig. 4   Representative examples of reflow equipment.

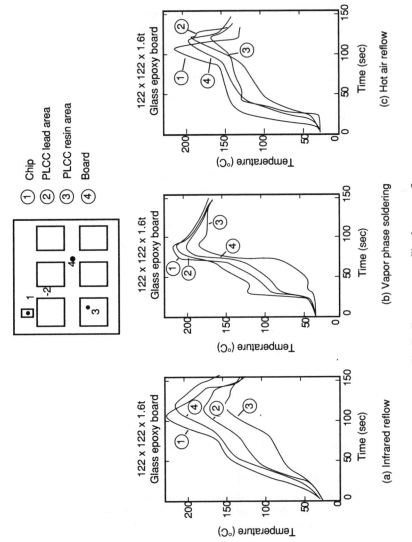

Fig. 5 Temperature profiles for mass reflow.

Legend:
① Chip
② PLCC lead area
③ PLCC resin area
④ Board

(a) Infrared reflow — 122 x 122 x 1.6t Glass epoxy board

(b) Vapor phase soldering — 122 x 122 x 1.6t Glass epoxy board

(c) Hot air reflow — 122 x 122 x 1.6t Glass epoxy board

135

or the temperature may not rise sufficiently at bonds shadowed from the heat by the components themselves.

Vapor Phase Soldering

Vapor phase soldering (VPS) uses the heat from the vapors of a hot, fluorinated, inactive solvent to cause the solder to melt and reflow. Because the heat conductor has a specific boiling point and the vaporized latent heat is great, the uniformity and rapidity of heating is outstanding. Moreover, the temperature will not rise beyond the boiling point of the solvent. However, maintenance of the device's complex structure and the running cost of consumable solvent are big disadvantages for this process.

Hot Air Reflow

Hot air reflow involves heating air with a heater and forcing the heated air to circulate within the oven. The solder is melted and reflowed by the heat transferred from the hot air. The heat characteristics (i.e., uniformity) of hot air reflow fall midway between those of infrared and VPS methods. Compared with VPS, although there is a fear of oxidation occurring if heat is applied for long periods, hot air reflow has the advantage of being maintenance free.

Laser Soldering

Soldering is accomplished quickly with the high energy density of a laser, but the abrupt rise in temperature sometimes causes solder balls to form. Recently, multiple-point soldering has been made possible with the use of an optical fiber to split the laser beam.

Optical Beam Soldering

Optical beam soldering employs an elliptical reflecting mirror to gather light from a xenon lamp. Currently there is a device available that heats all four sides of a quad flat package (QFP) simultaneously. The directivity of the beam makes this process, like infrared soldering, susceptible to unreflowed areas if the light does not reach the shadowed areas of the components.

As can be seen from the discussion above, there currently is no general purpose reflow device available. The appropriate reflow method must be chosen by taking into account the thermal capacity, type of mounted devices, and the production quantity of the subject assembly.

TABLE 1   The Pluses and Minuses of Soldering According to Lead Shape [1]

Item	Lead shape		
	Gull Wing	J-lead	Butt Lead
Increased lead count	***	*	**
Thinning package	***	*	**
Lead bends	*	***	**
Self-aligning effect	***	**	*
Ability to solder by many methods	***	*	*
Check after soldering	***	*	**
Cleaning	***	**	**

***, extremely good; **, good; *, bad

SOLDERING OF PACKAGES

Surface mount packages can be divided largely into leadless type, represented by leadless chip carriers (LCC) and leaded type, represented by QFPs and plastic-leaded chip carriers (PLCC). In high-density applications, leaded packages absorb stress better, have a finer connecting pitch, and exhibit better solderability. As can be seen from Table 1, even within leaded packages, gullwing QFPs have the highest lead counts.

As an example of the findings from an examination of quality in high-density soldering, we will present an overview of the surface characteristics of a soldered QFP having a lead pitch of 0.65 mm.

First, the appearance of a proper lead joint and its cross-section are shown in Fig. 6. It can be seen here that the solder conforms well to the small contact edges to make a good join.

Nearly all leads are made up of iron–nickel alloy because lead strength must presently be retained in fine leads. The results from evaluating the joint strength using a peel test are shown in Fig. 7. The strength of the joint is affected by both the shape of the fillet and the mechanical characteristics of the surface. As can be seen from the figure, the reflow temperature (a process parameter), the lead's surface state, and the volume of solder all affect the strength of the joint [2].

On the other hand, looking closely at the copper pad, which is the board's bond surface, shows an approximately 1.5 μm alloy layer formed (see Fig. 8). It is said that this is Cu_6Sn_5 (η phase) and Cu_3Sn (ε phase), but when slightly over-heated, ε phase grows greater, showing tendencies of embrittlement in the soldering characteristics.

(a) Mounted appearance

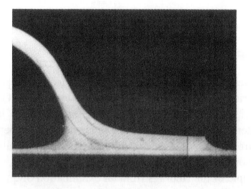

(b) Cross-section of bonded area

Fig. 6   Example of bonded quad flat package high-density lead.

Soldering defects that tend to occur with these packages include bridges, voids, and fillet defects. Examples of these defects are shown in Fig. 9. The causes of these defects and corrective action are discussed below.

Bridges

Solder bridges are caused mostly by the solder paste itself losing its shape during solder paste printing, component placing, or the heating process. Management of printing accuracy along with use of solder paste that maintains its shape are required and are important tasks for printer manufacturers and solder paste makers. Because lead spacings are growing increasingly finer to support demands for ever higher densities, the time has come where radical measures are needed to achieve a consistent bridge-free assembly.

	Solder plating	Temperature (°K)	Solder paste print thickness (μm)
(A)-1	O	488	200
(A)-2	O	488	130
(B)-1	X	488	200
(B)-2	X	528	200

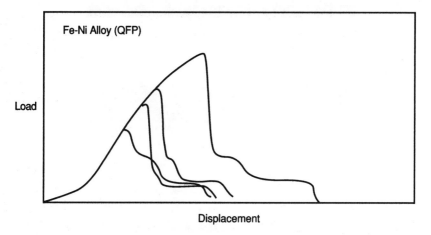

Fig. 7   Load on quad flat package (QFP) lead bond area—displacement curve.

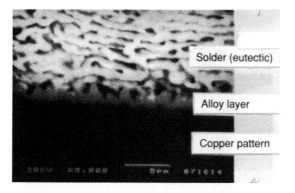

Fig. 8   Scanning electron micrograph of bond surface.

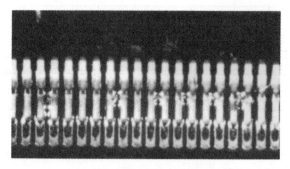

(a) Bridge (external photograph)

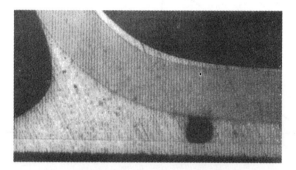

(b) Void (cross-sectional photograph)

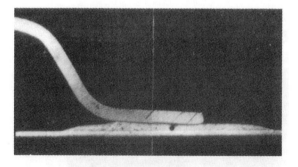

(c) Fillet defect

Fig. 9   Examples of soldering defects.

Voids

The specific cause of voids is unclear, but in many cases the void is spherical, as shown in Fig. 9. This type of void is thought to be the remains of the vaporized component within the flux. Voids tend to occur when heat is applied rapidly or when the solder melt time is especially short, although this is dependent on the brand of solder paste used. A temperature profile is needed that melts the solder after the flux has reached a sufficiently active state and which solidifies the solder only after the vaporized component of the flux has adequately escaped.

Fillet Defects

Insufficient heat and defects in cleaning or activating the material surfaces cause fillet defects. With mass reflow, the temperature has a tendency to be insufficient for components that have a high thermal capacity. In contrast, because ε phase grows when small components receive excessive heat, choosing a heat source that exhibits uniform heat properties is important. Also, by selecting a high-activity flux, more consistent cleaning can be obtained. When considering the corrosion reliability of the product, it is vital that the components and boards be managed under fixed conditions (see Fig. 10).

Bridges, voids, and fillet defects are the main soldering problems seen with QFPs. Aside from these defects, lead lifts are becoming a serious problem with fine leads. These lead lifts cause opens and inadequate fillets, defects that potentially can result in product failures. Because these defects are difficult to detect during inspections, there is a tendency among manufacturers to apply solder just a bit thicker than the optimum amount so that the solder fills to make up for lifted leads. This is disadvantageous from the standpoint of preventing bridges. An even stricter standard for manufacturing accuracy of component leads is necessary.

Although the defects noted above usually appear immediately after soldering, in many cases good joint contact and strength exist in the early stages, but the product becomes defective due to the extended heat cycle incurred during use. Also, residue flux indicates the hygroscopic property and leads to surface leaks and corrosion, which in turn cause failure.

Accordingly, in order to guarantee soldering reliability it is necessary to 1) choose component materials and a suitable design befitting the product's specifications, 2) establish a high degree of control of the processes focusing on soldering, and 3) introduce inspection and testing that can precisely guarantee quality.

CONCLUSION

The discussion above deals with surface mount technology from the perspective of component soldering. Progress in compacting and incorporating higher func-

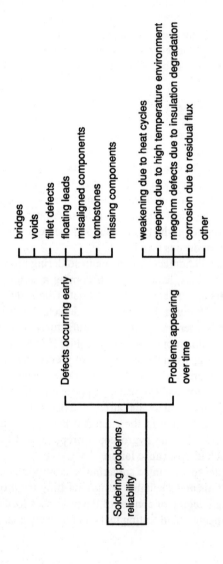

Fig. 10 Classification of degradation and soldering defects.

tionality into a product will continue in the future, demanding ever smaller bonds and higher yields in bond technology. We are still waiting for the appearance of an innovative bond technology independent of soldering with solder paste.

REFERENCES

[1] Ishiguro, *Electronic Technology,* March 1988, p. 33.

[2] Nakaoka et al., *Welders Society,* Micro Bonding Research Committee Material MJ-84-87.

Solder Paste Reliability Technology at Production Sites

Manabu Harada

Malcom Co., Ltd.

INTRODUCTION

Solder paste control goes hand in hand with the demand for greater accuracy in surface mount technology (SMT) and can be summed up into four key points, in order of their use in the solder paste processes: 1) print quality, 2) tackiness, 3) solderability, and 4) low residue properties.

Print quality involves controlling the thixotropic index and viscosity of the paste as it undergoes stress mechanisms when being transferred across the stencil. Tackiness is the control of adhesive strength to overcome vibrations that would cause chips to be displaced or fall off the board. Solderability entails the control of wetting time, solder balls, and spreading. Low residue properties are determined by the amount of flux residue ions and the insulation resistance. This is particularly important because of the trend toward no-cleaning fluxes.

These four control points for production sites must not rely solely on intuition and experience, but should be guided by numerical analysis and measurement. It can be said that only with these tools can repeatable and reliable control be achieved. This paper focuses on solder paste analysis and measurement methods in relation to each of the control points.

PRINT QUALITY

The point of solder paste print control is to decrease defects caused by solder slumping, chips, contaminants, stencil clogging, and solder drawn to the stencil's underside. In effect, it is the pursuit of increasing the number of good prints. Very important to print control are repeatability and mechanical accuracy, such as the alignment of the stencil pattern to the board's pads, squeegee print speed, squeegee pressure, and snap off. Beyond this, the properties of the paste itself are important. With this in mind, the relationships between the above-noted defects and the viscosity of the solder paste are discussed below.

Solder Paste Viscosity

Figure 1 shows the viscosity of six types of solder paste (P1 to P6) as measured by a Malcom PCU-2 viscometer. The x axis shows the viscometer rotational speed, N, and the shear rate D in proportion to N. The y axis shows the viscosity, η. Viscosity is defined by equation (1), where τ is the shearing stress incurred when the paste is sheared at rate D.

$$\eta = \tau/D \qquad (1)$$

As can be seen from Fig. 1, as D increases, the viscosity decreases linearly, making it impossible to grasp all characteristics of the paste's viscosity from only the data obtained at a specific shear rate. Here, the direction of this linear line is defined as the thixotropic index T_1. T_1 can be derived with equation (2).

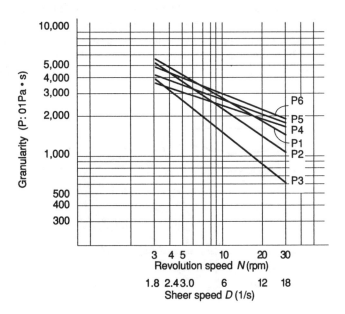

Fig. 1 Granularity data on six types of paste (P1 to P6).

$$T_1 = \log (\eta_1/\tau_2) \,/\, \log (D_2/D_1) \qquad (2)$$

Using a squeegee speed sufficient to transfer paste from the stencil to the board in a model equation, the viscosity is expressed as η_{600} when D is equal to 600. From this, viscosity can be found from equation (3) when D is arbitrary.

$$\eta = 10 \,(k - T_1 \cdot \log D) \qquad (3)$$

Constants k and T_1 are derived from the known values D_1, D_2, η_1 and η_2.

Stencil Penetration

Figure 2 illustrates how the solder paste rolls across the stencil when pushed by the squeegee and fills the stencil openings. The stress received by the paste on the stencil surface is represented by τ. The angle of contact between the stencil surface and the squeegee is represented by θ. Because the paste is pressed into the stencil openings at a high squeegee print speed, it can be said that the print quality is related to the degree of η_{600} viscosity noted above.

In other words, if η_{600} is large, the paste resists the squeegee rubber, increasing the amount pressed into the stencil openings. This increases the resulting line widths and film thickness. If too large, slumping occurs or openings are missed, resulting in chips. Conversely, if η_{600} is small, the resulting line widths and film thickness are reduced. If too small, it causes sags and stringing. However, as Fig. 3 shows, if the alignment discrepancy between the pattern and the board pads is large, slumping, contamination, and paste drawn to the stencil's underside cannot be avoided. Nevertheless, the seal formed by the fit between the stencil and board contours is lost with excessive squeegee pressure or inappropriate snap off. To achieve a consistent print, the paste's viscosity must be con-

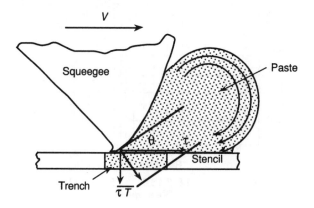

Fig. 2 Solder paste being inserted into the stencil trench.

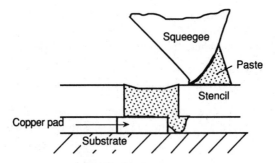

Fig. 3 Misalignment of stencil to pad, which causes slumping and leaking to back-
side of mask.

trolled, assuming a stable print with high accuracy alignment and a suitable
squeegee pressure. The value η_{600} is used for calculations, but it is not easy to
use at the production site; in reality, control of thixotropic index T_1 and viscosity
η_6 when squeegee speed D is equal to 6 is adequate.

Stencil Extraction

Figure 4 shows the forces acting on the paste in the stencil openings when
the stencil is removed from the board. The paste tends to remain in the openings
because of the shearing stress τ at the opening's edges. On the other hand, the
paste's cohesion T stemming from the pad's adhesive strength works to pull the
paste to the board. This struggle is resolved only when $T \gg \tau$. Whether the paste
releases from the stencil or not rests solely in this relationship. Nothing, however,
can be done about the clogging that results from jagged opening edges.

Just as the viscosity depended on the shear rate, the cohesive force relies on
the rate at which the stencil is pulled away from the board. Here, let the speed at

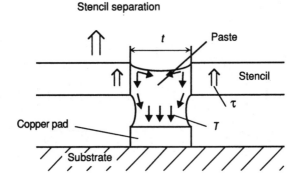

Fig. 4 Stencil removal.

which the stencil is removed be η_a, the cohesion during removal be T_a, and the edge stress be τ_a. The force with which paste is pulled from the stencil can be found with equation (4), where the stencil opening height is h, the width w, and the length l.

$$W = ltT_a - 2h\,(l+t)\,\tau_a \tag{4}$$

The larger W is in equation (4), the better the paste will release from the stencil. Next, τ_a is found with equation (5) by substituting $\eta = \tau/D$ into equation (3).

$$\tau_a = D \times 10^{(k \cdot T_1 \cdot \log D)} \tag{5}$$

From equation (4) we find that the paste pulls away from the stencil well when the cohesive force is large, the viscosity is low at a high shear rate, the stencil is thin, and the area of the stencil opening is large.

TACKINESS

Tackiness refers to the combined force of the cohesion and adhesion noted earlier. In many cases, chips are held on the board by the paste's tackiness during reflow. It is at this time that defects occur from chips falling off the board or by being displaced by the vibration of the chip placer or conveyor. In particular, defects increase when parts are mounted after some time has elapsed since printing or when tackiness is reduced by reflow heat.

Measuring a paste's tackiness must take into account the placing rate of the placing equipment. The reason for this is shown in Fig. 5. Leads or contact surfaces pressed into the paste at high speed overcome the paste's yield value and cause it to flow. This means that the thixotropic structure of the paste is destroyed, causing the paste's flux and particles to flow well, thus ultimately increasing the contact area with the leads. However, as shown in Fig. 5, if the leads are pressed

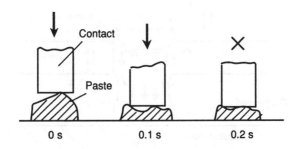

Fig. 5 Paste fluidity condition during mounting.

into the paste rapidly with little force, the contact after 0.1 s is incomplete. After 0.2 s, the lead stops penetrating the paste, allowing a thixotropic structure to reform. In short, the contact surface does not expand beyond this point. If tackiness is measured in this state by pulling on the leads, the tackiness would decrease to the extent that the contact surface has decreased. Many chip placers actually mount chips in this way rather than carefully pressing each chip into the paste. If chips are placed immediately after the paste is printed, this is not a major problem. But if time is allowed to pass, the paste surface dries out and the tackiness decreases for the reasons shown in Fig. 5.

In light of this, in regard to measuring tackiness, the prescribed IPC standard, SPC-819, is not well suited in its current state. Measuring tackiness by preloading a contact 5.1 mm in diameter for 5 s and then pulling up at a rate of 2.5 mm/s does not match today's placing machine movements. This has been confirmed with actual testing.

For these reasons, we have measured tackiness (with a Malcom FG-1 solder tester) for a placing time of 0.2 s and a pull-away rate of 10 mm/s. Figure 6 shows the results of measuring up to 30 hours at a press force of 120 gf and 40 gf the tackiness of a paste reportedly capable of accepting parts placed 24 hours after printing. As can be seen from Fig. 6, the paste can be used for up to 26 hours. Additionally, according to the measuring device, the reflow temperature can be set freely by a heater, making it possible to measure the reduction in tackiness caused during heating.

SOLDERABILITY

Control of solderability cannot be adequately done by merely measuring wettability of presoldered leads as in dip solder. As the solder paste turns from a solid state to a liquid state, the entire process involves solderability. The keys to control are wettability, solder balls, and wetting time.

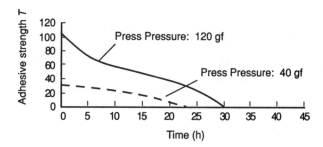

Fig. 6 Paste adhesion strength measurement results.

Wettability

Solder paste wettability is realistically measured by a spread test method rather than by a stress test via meniscograph. This method determines the size of wetted corners by the rectilinear diameter of the melted solder printed on a copper plate. Therefore, it can be said that the larger the wetted diameter, the better the wettability. This wetting spread test can actually be performed by cleaning a 0.5-mm-thick copper plate with alcohol and printing solder paste with a 0.2-mm-thick stencil with openings 6.5 mm in diameter. Next, a heater set to 235° C is placed on the copper plate for 5 s, cooled, and then the spread is measured.

Solder Balls

Solder balls occur when surface-oxidized balls of paste settle as the flux gas evaporates during solder fusion. Solder paste control to prevent solder balls relies on tests such as for wettability. However, instead of a copper plate, an aluminum plate is used. After the paste fuses, the presence of solder balls is observed with a 20× magnifying glass.

Wetting Time

Knowing the temperature when the solder begins to melt and the number of seconds required for the paste to wet the leads is important for paste control. Reflow oven temperature profiles are finely designed and are useful in analyzing and preventing tombstoning by board surface temperature distribution deviations.

The measurement of wetting time is done with the adhesive strength tester noted earlier. First, the contact is pressed into the paste printed on the copper plate and then heated. Next, the temperature and temporal change in adhesive strength acting on the contact while the paste is melting are measured.

LOW RESIDUE PROPERTIES

Lastly, achieving a low residue is becoming a major control issue with the move toward clean fluxes in the aim of discontinuing the use of fluorocarbons. Nevertheless, current methods to measure residue quantity take a lot of time and are not suitable for use at the production site.

Ion Quantity Measurement

This method involves measuring the amount of sodium chloride per unit area after reflow as an indication of the quantity of ionized residue remaining on the board.

Corrosion Due to Residue

The presence of corrosion can be detected by observation while applying heat and humidity. The board is left for 72 hours under an atmosphere of 40° C with a relative humidity of 93%.

Insulation Resistance Test

In a like way, insulation resistance is measured by applying after reflow a direct bias under humidification and high temperatures and then leaving it for long periods. In concrete terms, a comb-like pattern of conductors spaced 0.3 mm apart is reflowed then, while energizing with a 45 to 50 VDC current, it is left for 168 hours in an atmosphere of 40° C with 85 to 90% humidity. The insulation resistance is then measured at a test voltage of 100 VDC.

In any case, the difficulty of this measurement is greatly disproportionate to the importance of controlling residue and is likely to continue to be a problem in the future.

Reliability Technology for Soldering

Seimi Ishii

Sony Corp., Haneda Technology Center

INTRODUCTION

Recent advances in high-density surface mount technology have led to the extensive use of ultra-high-pin-count devices (quad flat packages [QFP], VQFP) and miniature chips (1.6×0.8 mm, 1.0×0.5 mm). As a result, the conventional solder coating method used on printed wiring substrates for surface mounting is causing the frequent occurrence of solder defects in high density surface mounting processes.

We analyzed why soldering defects occur with such high frequency, and developed a new surface processing method (heat resistant preflux processing) to overcome soldering defects. Described below is the soldering defect analysis and an overview of the heat resistant preflux process.

ANALYSIS OF SOLDERING DEFECTS

Solder coat processing is characterized by large variations in the thickness of the applied coat, which causes the following soldering defects in highly dense surface mount applications.

When the Solder Coat Is Too Thick

As Fig. 1 shows, the lands for QFP ICs and VQFP ICs are designed with extremely fine spacing (0.3- to 0.5-mm pitch). Thus, when compared with nor-

(a) When the solder coat is thick

Bridges occur because of the fine
pitch of QFP and VQFP terminals

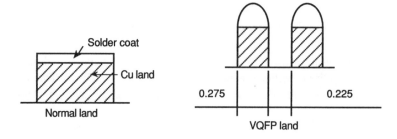

(b) When the solder coat is thin

Solder paste wetting defects

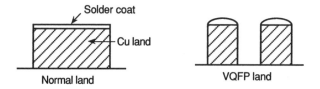

The surface becomes Sn rich and
oxidizes with the reflow heat

Fig. 1 Problems with solder coat processing.

mal lands, the solder coat on these lands becomes thicker because of surface tension. This results in print defects (smears) occurring more easily when printing solder paste. Also, the combined coat thickness of the solder coat layer and the solder paste layer becomes thicker. With the land pitch as fine as it is, solder bridges occur with a high frequency during reflow.

When the Solder Coat Is Too Thin

In trying to make the solder coat of the lands for QFP ICs and VQFP ICs thinner, the coat becomes quite thin (5 μm or less) in comparison with normal lands, making these surfaces tin-rich. When the lands become tin-rich, the reflow heat causes surface oxidation and the occurrence of solder paste wetting defects.

In these ways, the coat thickness varies greatly on solder-coat–processed substrates, causing solder bridges where the coat is thick and solder paste wetting defects where the coat is thin. Because of these problems, solder coat processing is not suited to high-density surface mount applications.

Solder Coat Thickness and Surface Analysis

Our analysis consisted of changing the solder coat thickness and observing the surface conditions with a scanning electron microscope (SEM). This was further analyzed with an XMA device. Figure 2 shows the surface conditions observed.

When the solder coat thickness is 5 µm or less, the surface is nearly all tin and it oxidizes when a fairly high reflow temperature is applied, thereby decreasing wettability. For this test, the oven was set to 200° C and the substrate was heated for 10 minutes, making the heating process equivalent to reflowing three times.

Next we found that when the solder coat thickness is approximately 10 µm, in addition to tin, small fragments of lead can be observed on the surface. When this is heated, the lead regions gather to form larger fragments, but because the tin occupies a large surface area, the solder paste wettability is still insufficient.

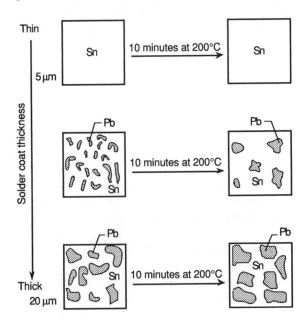

Fig. 2 Surface condition of the solder coat.

We then found that when the solder coat thickness is approximately 20 µm, the lead fragments become larger and do not change greatly when heated. Therefore, the solder paste wettability is good.

Figure 3 shows an SEM photograph and the XMA analysis results of a 5-µm-thick solder coat after heating. The ratio of lead to tin is 1:26, making the content of tin extremely high and the solder paste wettability poor (analyzed at the area indicated by the arrow).

Figure 4 shows an SEM photograph and the XMA analysis results of a 20-µm-thick solder coat after heating. The ratio of lead to tin is 1:4, making the lead content high and the solder paste wettability good.

Based on the above findings, we then performed a test to verify that the solder paste wettability is poor in places where the solder coat is thin. The results of this test are shown in Figs. 5 and 6. We looked at solderability of the area marked by the arrow by passing a substrate with a thin solder coat through the reflow process once. We then printed solder paste and reflowed again. In Fig. 5a, the solder paste wettability is poor, causing the solder to migrate up the component leads to leave nothing but tin on the copper lands. In Fig. 6a, the solder paste has collected near the center for the same reason.

In summary, we found large variations in the solder coat thickness, causing poor wettability at thin areas and solder bridges at thick areas. However, in its present form, solder coat thickness is difficult to control for two reasons: 1) the shape of the component lands on the substrate are diverse; and 2) a fundamental problem exists in the solder leveller used to form the solder coat. From these conclusions, we developed heat resistant preflux processing for future high-density surface mounting.

PRESENT SUBSTRATE SURFACE PROCESSING METHODS

There are two methods to date of processing the substrate surface, as noted in Table 1.

Preflux Processing

The first method involves the use of natural or composite resin-based materials to act as an oxidation inhibitor on the copper lands in the time interval between substrate fabrication and component mounting. Consequently, the solder adheres only with the combination of a preflux and postflux applied prior to the solder dip. However, because there is no thermal resistance, this method does not hold up to reflow heat. It is used on general purpose single-sided and double-sided bare hole substrates.

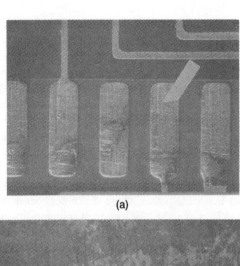

(a)

(b) × 5 K

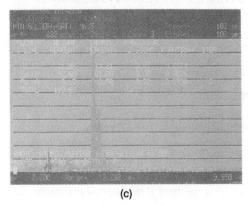

(c)

Fig. 3   SEM photograph of 5-μm-thick solder coat after heating.

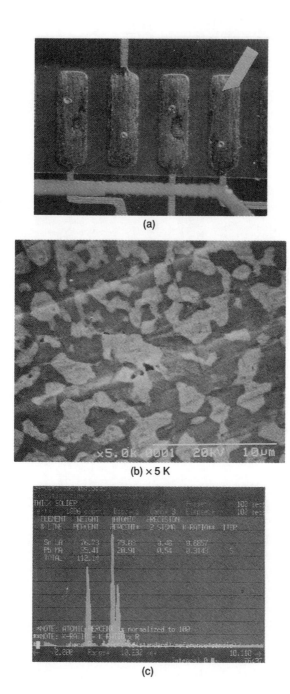

Fig. 4 SEM photograph of 20-μm-thick solder coat after heating.

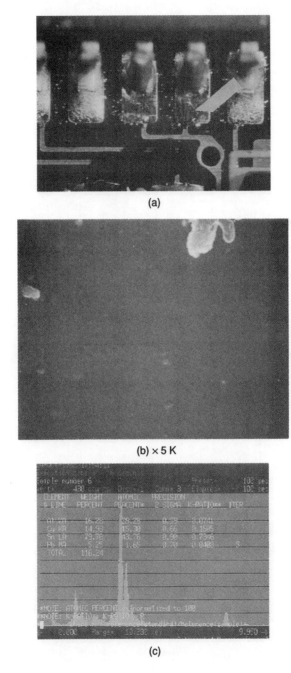

(a)

(b) × 5 K

(c)

Fig. 5   Areas of poor wettability after printing solder paste and reflowing.

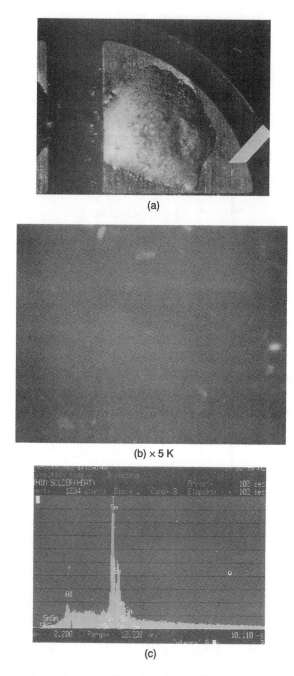

(a)

(b) × 5 K

(c)

Fig. 6 Areas of poor wettability after printing solder paste and reflowing.

TABLE 1   Previous Methods of Copper Foil Surface Processing

Preflux processing

Role:	Acts as a rust inhibitor from substrate fabrication to solder dip of surface mount components
Use:	Single-sided substrates, double-sided bare hole substrates, etc. • Can't withstand reflow temperatures

 For reflow soldering

Solder coat processing

Role:	Acts as preflux and prevents copper land tarnishing during reflow
Use:	Double-sided through-hole substrates and multilayer substrates
Problems:	Thickness variation causes solder bridges and incomplete soldering on high-density surface mount substrates.

Heat-resistant preflux processing

Solder Coat Processing

As noted above, solder coat processing is a metal oxidation-inhibiting coat process using molten solder. It serves as a preflux and also prevents tarnishing of the copper lands at the reflow process. This method is used widely on multilayer substrates and double-sided through-hole substrates that can be reflowed. However, because the solder coat thickness varies greatly, it is not well suited for high-density surface mount applications.

DEVELOPMENT OF HEAT-RESISTANT PREFLUX PROCESSING

In order to get the most from the heat-resistant preflux process on high-density surface mount substrates, two conditions are essential: 1) the solder coat must be thin and uniform; and 2) the heat-resisting properties must be maintained so that there is no decrease in solder wettability during reflow.

Condition 1) was the point of departure for development. The preflux processing described previously is one way to fulfill condition 1). We established heat-resistant preflux processing techniques after resolving the cause of low heat resistance under normal preflux processing.

Discussion of the development points and process know-how is abbreviated for purposes of this paper. To give an indication of the superior level of the heat-resisting properties, Fig. 7 shows the results of the differential thermal analysis. The change in weight after heating for 60 minutes at 200° C was a mere 2% for heat-resistant preflux, compared with a 12% change with present preflux materials.

Figure 8 shows one example of solder defect rates, comparing solder coat processing and preflux processing. Shown here are the percentages of solder bridge defects in VQFP ICs using a substrate for an 8-mm video camcorder. The number of defects with preflux processing is approximately 1/6 that for solder coat processing. In this way, heat resistant preflux processing reduces solder defects in high-density surface mount applications.

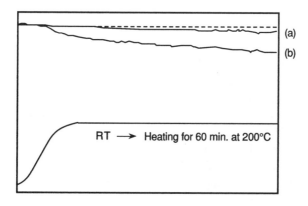

(a) Heat resistant preflux weight change: 2%
(b) Currently used preflux weight change: 12%

Fig. 7 Weight variations found by differential thermal analysis (DAT-TG).

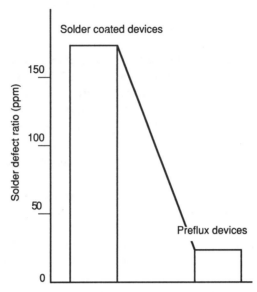

Fig. 8   Chip mount quality on 8 mm VCR substrate.

As a frame of reference, Fig. 9 illustrates the differences in solderability between heat-resistant preflux substrates and normal preflux substrates. These substrates were passed twice through the reflow process (peak temperature of 250° C) and then put through a solder dip. It can easily be seen that the heat-resistance properties of the heat-resistant preflux substrate are superior.

CONCLUSION

Heat resistant preflux processing is an extremely effective means for decreasing the number of solder defects in high-density surface mount applications. At Sony, we have come to use widely these heat-resistant preflux substrates in such products as our TR-55 handycam, which uses a 4-layer, high-density surface mount substrate. We believe that heat-resistant preflux processing techniques will spread throughout the industry as surface mount technology advances.

On the other hand, taking a mid- to long-range view, we must examine no-clean fluxes and solder pastes, and move toward solderless processing (i.e., a new surface process and connection technology for substrates) to deal with environmental problems and problems in printing solder paste on substrates for mounting fine-pitch, high-pin-count ICs and ultra-small chip components.

(a) Heat -resistant preflux substrate

(b) Normal preflux substrate

Fig. 9 Photograph of solderability (reflowed twice and solder dipped).

Part 4

Tape Automated Bonding

Bump Inspection and Evaluation Technology

Kenzo Hatada

Matsushita Electric Industrial Co., Ltd.
Semiconductor Research Center

INTRODUCTION

This is an investigation of inspection methods for chips with metal bumps that pass through the barrier metal on top of the semiconductor chip aluminum electrodes. In general, the major inspections for bumped chips are:

1. bump characteristics, and
2. electrical characteristics of the chip through the bumps (Fig. 1).

Four bump characteristics that require inspection are barrier resistance, shear strength, hardness, and shape. Barrier resistance inspection is necessary when the

---

Characteristic inspections of the bump itself

(a) Barrier resistance

(b) Bump shear

(c) Bump hardness

(d) Bump shape

Electrical inspection

Fig. 1 Types of bump inspection.

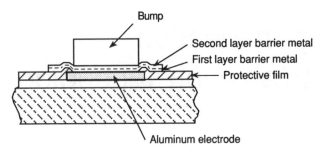

Fig. 2 Bump structure.

bump formation process is aided by the barrier metals. A rather high contact resistance can exist between layers of barrier metals. Bump shear strength inspection is basic to bump formation. If a particular level of shear strength cannot be guaranteed, the bump is deemed unusable. Bump shape inspection involves a visual inspection of the bump and the inspection of bump height after plating. The visual inspection mainly involves the use of a microscope to detect fragmented bumps and short circuits between adjacent bumps. Bump height inspection measures the distribution of bump height (plating thickness) on the chip. Bump hardness inspection measures the hardness of the bumps.

Results from these bump inspections not only feed back without pause into the continuous wafer production process for process stabilization, but are also used to determine if the bumped wafer is defective.

Electrical inspection is basically identical to the probe inspection that takes place at the completion of the semiconductor processes. The same probe cards and probers are used as in the semiconductor process. Electrical inspection of the wafer takes place after the bump inspection has been completed. After electrical inspection, the wafer is diced and bonded to the inner leads of the TAB tape.

BUMP INSPECTION METHODS

Bump inspection is used to evaluate the bump formation process (i.e., barrier metal formation, bump plating, etching, and other processes). In general, it involves a sampling inspection of the wafer after bump formation and measures several locations on the wafer. In contrast, electrical inspection encompasses the entire wafer and all of the chips.

Bump Inspection

Barrier Resistance. Figure 2 shows the structure of the bump. Barrier resistance occurs readily between each metal layer, the largest resistance being between the aluminum electrode and the first layer (titanium or chromium film). Two methods can be used to measure barrier resistance. Figure 3a shows the four-terminal method, in which a constant current is applied between two bumps and the electrical potential between the two bumps is measured. In general, this method is widely used, but because the measured barrier resistance includes an aluminum wiring resistance component, slight errors are easily incurred. Figure 3b shows the three-terminal method. Unlike the four-terminal method, it is not necessary to consider the aluminum wiring resistance component. A constant current of under 1 mA is used to measure the barrier resistance. The barrier resistance fluctuates depending on factors such as the barrier metal material (titanium or chromium), adhesion conditions, and aluminum electrode surface processing and ranges from one to several tens of $m\Omega/3,000 \ \mu m^2$. Semiconductor chips that require a low barrier resistance are LSIs that handle a relatively large current

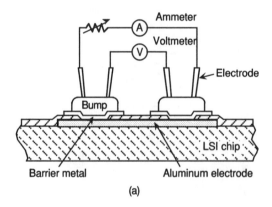

(a)

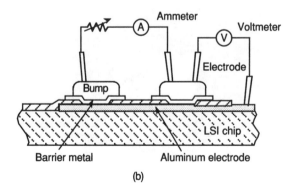

(b)

Fig. 3   Barrier resistance measurement methods (examples).

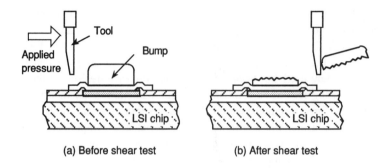

(a) Before shear test   (b) After shear test

Fig. 4   Shear measurement.

Fig. 5   Shear measurement equipment. (Lesca PTR-01)

(several tens of mA), such as for thermal printers and LED arrays. A large barrier resistance causes a drop in voltage, which produces inconsistency in printing density or luminance. Thus, the conditions for barrier metal formation are critical for chips that handle large current.

There is no specialized equipment for measuring barrier metal resistance. Normally, a manually operated probe is used to measure the bumps at five to ten different locations on the wafer.

Bump Shear Strength. Bump shear strength is an important inspection because shear strength directly affects the level of reliability. Evaluating shear strength involves measuring the force needed to break off the bump when pushing it from the side, as well as measuring the breakage mode at the surface of the break (see Fig. 4).

For shear strength measurement, the dedicated shear strength measurement apparatus shown in Fig. 5, a commercially available product that can measure both shear strength and lead pull tests, can be used. There is also a simple method that involves attaching a minute insertion needle to the tip of the tension gauge. The tip of this insertion needle is used to apply a shear force to the bump. The value on the tension gauge can then be read. Errors in the break mode are easily produced if the distance between the chip surface and the tool used to measure the shear force is not correctly set. Figure 6 shows the four breakage modes that can result from a shear test.

In the A1 mode, the break occurs between the barrier metal and the bump, or between the aluminum electrode and the barrier metal. The cause of the separation is the area of low strength that exists between the barrier metal and the bump, which in turn is dependent on the surface condition of the barrier metal and the plating conditions used for bump formation. It is necessary to correct barrier metal and bump formation conditions because this separation is not an indication of good shear strength.

The C1 and C2 modes are the ideal break modes. In mode C1, the bump itself breaks, while in mode C2 the aluminum electrode breaks. Modes C1 and C2 occur when all the bump formation conditions are ideal.

The AS mode is an unfavorable breakage in which the chip is damaged. The AS mode is caused by a remarkably large stress within the barrier metal. In rare instances, it can be caused by a relatively thin aluminum electrode thickness of 4,000 angstroms, or by the use of low temperature chemical vapor deposition (CVD) in forming the insulation film under the aluminum electrode. It is necessary to reevaluate the bump formation process, including the wafer process.

Bump Hardness. Vickers hardness is primarily used to measure hardness. An ultra-fine Vickers hardness tester is used to form a pressure imprint on the bump surface (see Fig. 7). The size of this imprint is used to measure the hard-

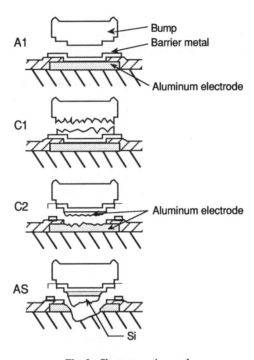

Fig. 6 Shear separation mode.

ness. High levels of hardness cause a large amount of internal stress that goes through the barrier metals and cracks the silicon dioxide and silicon under the aluminum electrode. Thermal processing at 250° to 400° C will reduce hardness. The best hardness level is between 40 and 60.

Bump Shape. Deformed bumps decrease reliability by reducing the inner lead bonding strength and exposing the barrier metal on the aluminum electrode. The generation of defectively shaped bumps is almost entirely due to unsatisfactory resist pattern formation of the mask materials used for plating. Inspection of the bump shape is performed with a microscope, but bump thickness is measured with a surface roughness gauge. About five samples on the wafer are measured for bump thickness. However, on chips requiring a high level of reliability, it is necessary to inspect all bumps.

Electrical Inspection. Probe inspection is used to determine the electrical quality of the chips. A prober makes contacts with the bumps on each chip. Normally, a probe card is used, as shown in Fig. 8. The probe is either shaped like a needle, as shown in Fig. 9a or is a flat plate shape, as shown in Fig. 9b. However, because the bump itself is soft and easily damaged, flat plated probers are most

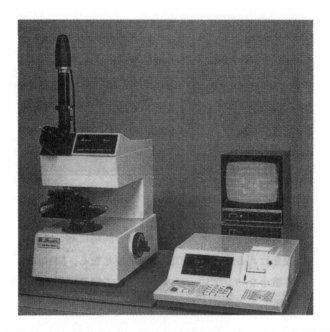

Fig. 7 Hardness tester. (Shimizu Dynamic Ultra Fine Hardness Tester DUH-50)

Fig. 8 Probe card example.

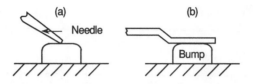

Fig. 9   Probe card needle shape.

often used. For electrical inspection it is possible to use the same inspection equipment used for wafer processing.

ISSUES AND PROSPECTS IN BUMP INSPECTION

Bump inspection can be divided into the sampling inspection of bump characteristics, and the electrical inspection of the entire chip. Bump dimensions are becoming smaller as LSI pitches become narrower. While 50-μm-pitch miniature bumps are near practical use, development of probers for miniature bumps and methods for bump height measurement remain major issues.

Miniature bumps can be damaged when touched by the probes of present probe cards. Thus, it is necessary to develop probe cards that have a soft touch on the bump surface. Moreover, with TAB technology, if variations in bump height are not reduced, the inner lead bonding (ILB) yield decreases. For example,

Fig. 10   Microbump example (30 μm diameter bumps).

because a conventional probe card is pressed down firmly on the bumps, height differences of adjacent bumps are not detected. Thus, the chip would pass the electrical test but produce a defective ILB bond.

Bump inspection equipment capable of performing electrical and bump shape inspection simultaneously is needed. At present, after electrical inspection with a probe, bump shape inspection is performed visually with a microscope. This shape inspection is simply a two dimensional inspection, not a three dimensional inspection for thickness.

As pitches become increasingly narrow and bumps are reduced in size (see Fig. 10), it is important to develop equipment that simultaneously performs electrical and bump shape inspections. The challenge of finding a way to probe the miniature bumps shown in Fig. 10 is underway.

We anticipate the rapid development of bump inspection equipment that not only has a soft touch, but also departs from conventional concepts.

Inspection and Evaluation of TAB Tape

Kenzo Hatada

Matsushita Electric Industrial Co., Ltd.
Semiconductor Research Center

INTRODUCTION

Tape automated bonding (TAB) tape (hereafter referred to as *film carrier tape*) is inspected and evaluated by the maker, not the user. Accordingly, techniques of inspection and evaluation are generally left entirely to the maker. In some cases involving tape of high precision or reliability, however, the user defines inspection and evaluation techniques for the maker to follow.

The minimum specifications required to manufacture the tape (e.g., tape width, perforation dimensions and intervals, and copper thickness) are now standardized and users are designing tape for in-house use based upon these standards.

Inspection and evaluation of film carrier tape encompasses visual inspection, which focuses on manufactured tape dimensions, and destructive testing, such as lead strength tests and lead bend tests. Items and conditions of these tests differ among makers. While the means of visual inspection are relatively well established, each maker employs unique methods for destructive testing because it essentially involves evaluating the tape itself.

FILM CARRIER TAPE INSPECTION AND EVALUATION TECHNIQUES

Inspection and evaluation of film carrier tape can be divided roughly into visual inspection and destructive tests. Within visual inspection, there are visual tests, performed with a microscope, and dimensional tests that measure the manufacturing accuracy of the tape. Destructive tests are sampling inspections and largely emphasize evaluating long-term reliability.

Visual Inspection

Visual inspection is conducted by microscope across the entire film carrier tape, one site at a time. This requires a great number of inspectors, thus making it the most demanding task for TAB tape makers.

The following items are checked during visual inspection:

1. breaks or shorts in the circuit pattern and leads,
2. deformations of the inner leads (bends),
3. presence of whiskers, and
4. contamination on the tape or lead surfaces.

Sites determined to be defective by these tests are punched.

In appearance testing, a binocular microscope is employed. Recently, microscopes have been developed that can view the topside and underside of the fixed tape without the tape having to be repositioned.

Breaks and shorts in the circuit pattern and leads mainly occur during photoetching of the tape. Inner lead deformations, however, occur during the inner lead bonding (ILB) process and, because they decrease yields, must be eliminated at this stage. These inner lead deformations take two forms: contact between neighboring leads and bends in the direction of the lead's thickness.

Whiskers occur in tin-plated leads but are difficult to spot without a high-magnification microscope. Removing tape with whiskers at the inspection stage would be meaningless because more whiskers are likely to grow later. Rather, the presence of whiskers demands a re-examination of the conditions under which the solder plating process is carried out. Figure 1 shows a scanning electron micrograph of a whisker—the defect users are most concerned about.

Contamination on the leads and tape surface are difficult to detect without close and careful examination. The mere presence of contamination on the tip of the leads where the bump is formed (see Fig. 2) reduces ILB reliability. Furthermore, residual etching fluid on the tape surface invites copper migration. Because this contamination is difficult to detect by visual inspection, its presence generally emerges during the customer's reliability testing or through market defects. Ultimately, film carrier tape appearance tests are still reliant on human vision.

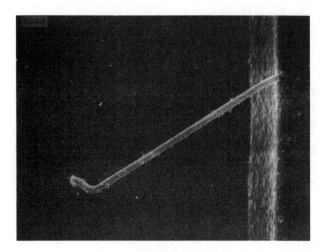

Fig. 1 Whiskers on a tin-plated lead.

Dimensional Testing

Dimensional testing involves two-dimensional measurements and three-dimensional measurements. The following items are included in two-dimensional measurements (see Fig. 3):

1. lead widths (inner leads and outer leads) {dimension A},
2. accumulative pitch of the leads {dimension B}, and
3. relative positioning among opposing leads {dimension C}.

Measurement is done with an optical measurement device and requires that the device have a minimum accuracy of 0.1 μm and a minimum measurable distance of 70 mm.

The inner lead width is measured where the leads attach to the bumps. When the leads are processed by wet etching, the lead's cross section takes the shape of a trapezoid, requiring that the direction of measurement be specified. Within a single reel of tape several points are measured along the leads of each site at three spots: at the beginning, the middle, and the end of the reel.

A large cumulative pitch error in the inner leads along one side of the device hole causes the inner leads to misalign with the bumps. A recent trend in LSI chips has been toward larger packages and finer pitch. But, for example, if a 15 mm chip has 140 pads on each side with 100 μm lead centers, an adjacent lead pitch error of 1 μm occurring in the film carrier tape's inner leads would result in

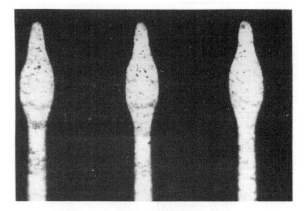

(a) Normal leads

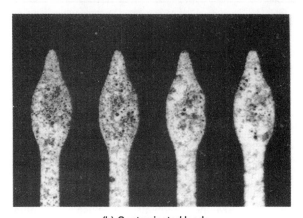

(b) Contaminated leads

Fig. 2   Contamination on the lead surface.

an accumulative pitch error from lead number 1 to lead number 140 of 140 μm. This amount of error would cause the inner leads to completely misalign with the bumps.

In a high-precision film carrier, this is a very critical dimension. Accumulative pitch error occurs easily from stress during the fabrication of the tape or from expansion and contraction of the base material or copper.

Pitch disparity between corresponding inner leads must always be inspected in large package LSI chips. The measurements of the accumulative pitch error and pitch disparity between inner leads are made with the film carrier tape fixed between two glass plates of high planarity.

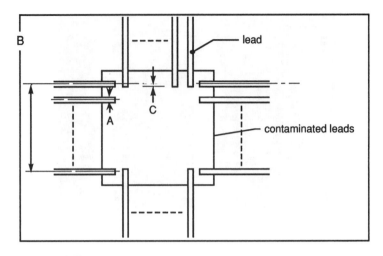

Fig. 3   Dimensional measurements of the film carrier tape.

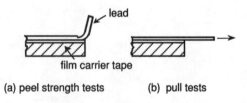

(a) peel strength tests   (b) pull tests

Fig. 4   Lead strength testing methods.

In addition to the above measurements, the device hole running in the feed direction and the theta disparity of the inner leads are measured. If the theta misalignment is large, automatic alignment during the inner lead bonding process is difficult.

Three-dimensional measurements include the film carrier tape thickness, the inner lead thickness, and the thickness of the plating. The inner lead thickness is measured by means of a normal micrometer; plate thickness is measured by a fluorescent x-ray device. The plate thickness at the inner lead bond is particularly important because the width at this area is narrow and encourages measurement error. For this reason, a dummy pattern for measuring the film thickness is constructed between sites to inhibit such measurement error. Actually, the plate thickness at the dummy pattern and at the inner lead area differ, so calibration is required. Particularly in gold–tin eutectic bonding with tin-plated tape, it is not the tin-plate thickness on the flat area of the leads but that on the sides of the leads that easily influences the amount of gold–tin eutectic alloy.

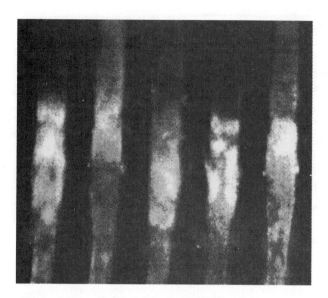

Fig. 5 Copper migration caused by contamination on the film lead.

With tin-plated leads spliced with a gold–tin eutectic alloy, the quantity of the gold–tin alloy easily influences the plating thickness at the sides of the leads, but not at the flat portions. Therefore, the leads are embedded with resin, and the plating thickness is measured by a cross grind of the lead. The results of these measurements show differing thicknesses at the flat portion and side portion of the lead.

Destructive Tests

Destructive tests are used to determine if the film carrier tape is at a level suitable for practical use and are made up almost entirely of reliability testing. Destructive tests include lead strength testing and moisture resistance testing. Lead strength testing involves peel strength tests and lead pull tests, shown in Fig. 4. Both of these tests are carried out after leaving the tape continuously in a high-temperature, high-humidity environment. The peel strength test primarily measures how strongly the copper adheres to the film tape. A measuring device designed specifically for this purpose does not exist, but either a shear strength tester, which is used to measure the shear strength of the bumps, or a simple tension gauge may be used.

Moisture resistance testing measures the electrical leak between leads on the tape when applying a bias voltage in an atmosphere of 85° C with 85% humidity, or 121° C with a barometric pressure of about 2. Fig. 5 shows copper

TABLE 1   Specifications of Automatic Inspection Systems

Item	Type I	Type II
Tape width	35, 70 mm	
Tape transport	reel-to-reel	
Number of cameras	1 (1 frame-1 field)	2 (1 frame-4 fields)
Inspection field of view	Maximum 8 × 8 mm	Maximum 15 × 15 mm
Accuracy	±5 μm (8 × 8 mm view)	±5 μm (15 × 15 mm view)
		±3 μm (8 × 8 mm view)
Lead width	40 μm or greater	
Inspection speed	Approximately 15 ms/lead	
Items inspected	Lead width (W), lead bend (B), lead pitch (P), disparity between corresponding leads (D), distance between leads (L)	
Outer dimensions	$1,600^W \times 800^D \times 1,750^H$	
Power	AC 100V; 50/60 Hz	
Options	Automatic marker/punch unit, host computer	

Fig. 6   TAB tape automatic inspection system.

migration that occurred under these types of conditions. The adjacent leads are completely shorted.

FUTURE THEMES AND PROSPECTS

The largest assignment for film carrier makers is the inspection and evaluation of processed goods. The automatic inspection system pictured in Fig. 6 was developed to automate visual inspection and possesses the performance noted in Table 1. Nevertheless, it must be further improved to detect three-dimensional lead bends and contamination. At the same time, this system must increase its processing speed as the lead count grows, because lengthy test times ultimately raise film carrier tape prices. It is believed that all visual inspection of the tape will eventually switch from human labor to automated machines like that shown in Fig. 6.

Tape widths increasing from 35 mm to 70 mm, device holes of 15 to 20 mm square, and lead pitches narrowing from 100 μm to the 50 to 60 μm range all place formidable demands from a tape manufacturing aspect. The question now is whether the precision mass production of tape fulfilling these requirements is possible.

Single Point Tab Technology for High-Pin-Count, Narrow-Lead-Pitch LSIs [1]

Hiroyuki Hirai

Toshiba Corp.

INTRODUCTION

In recent years, along with increasingly higher levels of integration, ICs have become larger in scale, higher in pin count, and narrower in lead pitch. In ten years, gate arrays are expected to reach the 1000- to 3000-pin class. The pad pitch limit of wire bonding (i.e., ball bonding), which is the most widely used IC interconnection method, is now 110 μm. Tape automated bonding (TAB) has attracted attention for its ability to interconnect pitches below 100 μm. Rapid progress is being made in shifting to tape carrier packages (TCPs) for liquid crystal driver ICs [2]. In addition, gang bonding is being used for inner lead bonding (ILB) because of its suitability to large scale mass production and its ability to reduce costs. There is, however, a trend toward increasing IC size due to the increasing I/O count, among other reasons. For inner lead gang bonding of chips larger than 13 mm^2, problems include difficulty in keeping the tool and stage level, a large increase in the load on the tool due to variations in bump height and higher pin counts, and difficulty in achieving uniform tool heating. These and other problems limit gang bonding. As a result, we investigated the use of SP-TAB ILB (single point TAB) for large scale, high-pin-count, narrow-pitch ICs. In the single point TAB method, each lead of the tape's inner leads is connected to a gold bump on an IC pad.

SP-TAB-ILB

Figure 1 illustrates the general idea of the SP-TAB-ILB method. Figure 2 is a photograph of the SP-TAB-ILB equipment used in the experiment. A thermosonic bonding method is used. Microcracks during bonding caused by the tool's impact load is reduced by decreasing the tool's drive distance. As shown in Fig. 3, the tip of the tool has a cross-shaped protrusion because the transmission of the ultrasonic vibration is along the line of the attachment to the transducer horn, that is, it vibrates along the Y axis. This eliminates variation in bonding strength as the bond tool is applied to each X, Y lead emerging from the tape's device hole [3]. The tip dimensions (the dimensions of the part that makes contact with the leads) of the tool used are almost identical to the dimensions of the bump. The X-Y table for driving the bonding head drive has linear motor control for high speed driving at 0.03 s/mm. The stopping precision is ± 0.01 mm, and the drive stroke is 100 × 70 mm.

EXPERIMENTAL SAMPLES

The specifications of the samples used in the experiment are as listed below.

1. IC dimensions: 16 × 16 × 0.45 mm
2. Gold bump dimensions: 65 × 75 × 16 μm, straight wall bumps
3. TAB tape: 70-mm width, 3-layer TAB tape (125-μm thick polyimide, adhesive, 35-μm thick copper foil)

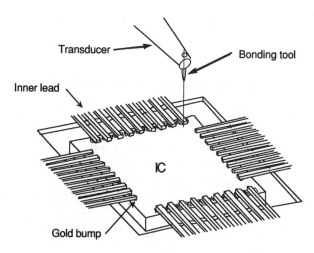

Fig. 1   Single-point TAB inner lead bonding (SP-TAB-ILB) conceptual diagram.

Fig. 2   The SP-TAB-ILB apparatus.

4. Lead surface processing: nickel = 0.8 μm, gold = 0.5 μm

5. Inner lead pitch: 90 μm

6. I/O pin count: 608

EXPERIMENTAL RESULTS AND CONSIDERATIONS

Determining Bonding Conditions

The parameters that influence the SP-TAB-ILB method bonds are bonding temperature (stage surface temperature), bonding load, ultrasonic power, and bonding time (duration of pressure). With these parameters taken as factors, experiments were performed to determine the bonding conditions through visual inspection of bonding strength and break mode. A pull test was used to determine bonding strength. An average bonding strength of greater than 20 gf and a lead break percentage of greater than 85% were taken as the standard. In order to achieve a high-speed bonding speed, the bonding time was fixed at 30 ms.

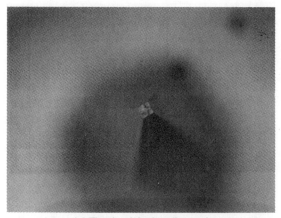

(a) The tip of the bonding tool

(b) Scanning electron micrograph of the bonding tool

Fig. 3   The bonding tool.

Figure 4 is a photograph of some bonds. Figure 5 shows a 608-pin TAB tape after bonding.

First we investigated bonding strength and break percentage as a function of bonding temperature at a fixed ultrasonic power level (0.25 W). Figure 6a shows these results. Over the established range an average bonding strength of higher than 20 gf was obtained, regardless of the temperature and load. However, a lead break percentage of greater than 85% was obtained in the 350 to 400° C range and when variance in bonding strength is taken into account, a temperature range of from 350 to 400° C was considered the most suitable for bonding.

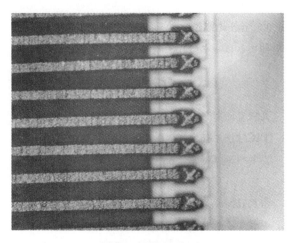

(a) Bonded inner leads

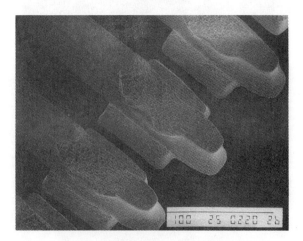

(b) Scanning electron micrograph of bonds

Fig. 4   Inner lead bonds.

Next we looked at bonding strength and lead break percentage as a function of ultrasonic power by setting the bonding temperature at 375° C. Figure 6b shows these results. Within the established range, an average bonding strength of greater than 20 gf was obtained regardless of the ultrasonic power and the load. However, the lead break percentage is only greater than 85% in the 0.25 to 0.30 W range and when variance in bonding strength is considered ultrasonic power in the 0.25 to 0.30 W range was considered the most suitable for bonding.

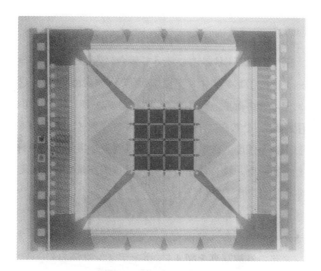

(a) The tape after inner lead bonding

(b) Enlarged view

Fig. 5 Single-point TAB bonding on a 608-pin TAB tape.

From the above results the bonding conditions used for this sample were as follows.

1. Bonding temperature: 350 to 400° C
2. Ultrasonic power: 0.25 to 0.30 W

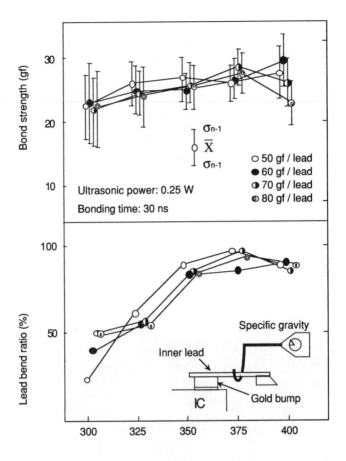

The relation between bonding temperature and pull strength

Fig. 6a The relation between bonding temperature, ultrasonic power, and pull strength (continued next page).

3. Bonding load: 50 to 80 gf/lead or bond
4. Bonding time: 30 ms

Bonding Strength and TAB Tape Lead Plating Thickness

A comparison was made of bonding strengths for TAB tape leads with differing plating thickness. The uniform bonding conditions used in the comparison were:

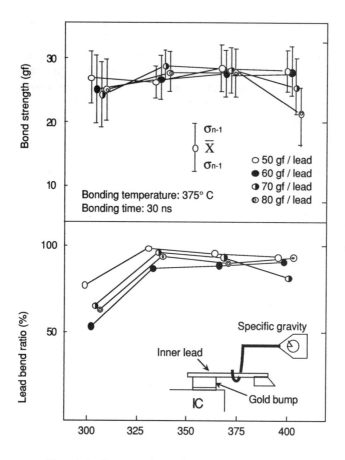

The relation between ultrasonic power and pull strength

Fig. 6a (continued)   The relation between bonding temperature, ultrasonic power, and pull strength.

1. Bonding temperature: 375° C
2. Ultrasonic power: 0.25 W
3. Bonding load: 50 gf/point
4. Bonding time: 30 ms

The TAB tape thicknesses compared in the experiment were:

1. nickel: 0.8 μm + gold: 0.5 μm
2. gold: 1.0 μm
3. gold: 5.0 μm

Figure 7 shows the relation between gold plating thickness and bonding strength and break percentage. These results show that under the same bonding conditions there is no significant difference in average bonding strength. In terms of lead break percentage, however, at a gold plating thickness of 5.0 μm, the percentage drops by 20 to 30% in comparison to the other cases. It can be assumed that this is due to the fact that at a gold plating thickness of 5.0 μm, the bond doesn't receive sufficient ultrasonic power. As a result, under these conditions a TAB tape

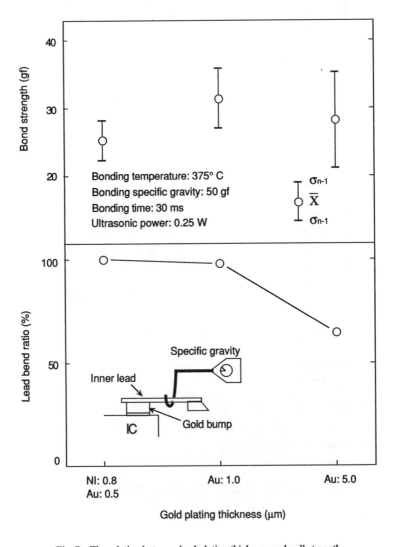

Fig. 7   The relation between lead plating thickness and pull strength.

lead gold plating thickness of 0.5 to 1.0 μm can be considered to be the most desirable.

Influence of Bonding Order on Positioning

We considered the influence that bonding order has on lead-to-bump alignment. In this experiment, two methods of bonding were performed and compared (see Fig. 8): Bonding method 1 starts by bonding one of the corner leads and then proceeds in order around the periphery of the IC. In bonding method 2, the eight pads at the four corners of the IC are bonded first in a sequence of alternating

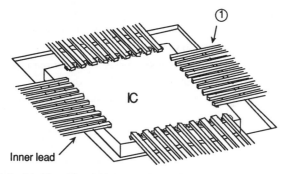

(a) Method 1: The pins sticking out from the IC periphery are bonded in order.

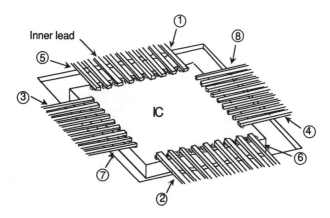

(b) Method 2: First the pads at the four corners of the IC are bonded, then the other pads are bonded.

Fig. 8   Two methods of bonding order.

opposite corners. Bonding method 1 can be applied without problem to small ICs in the 4 to 8 mm^2 range if the equipment is able to mechanically compensate for tape warpage and undulation. For ICs larger than 10 mm^2, however, particularly for 70 mm tape, the stress that the tool in method 1 brings to bear on a lead destroys the lead's overall stress balance and equilibrium is lost. This causes force to be applied to the tape itself in a rotary direction, which produces tape and lead slippage. For this reason, bonding method 2 is the preferable method.

TAB Tape Fixation Methods

One problem in applying SP-TAB-ILB to large-scale, narrow-pitch, high-pin-count ICs is the method of clamping the tape down. In this experiment, we investigated two methods, shown in Fig. 9.

In method 1, the tape's polyimide section is absorbed onto the tape stage, pressure is applied from above, and the tape is clamped. Method 2 uses the tape perforations. Tension is applied from the central axis of the tape's device hole in

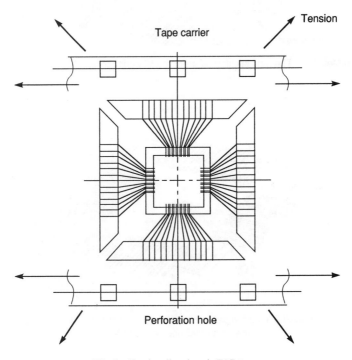

Fig. 9   Tension directions in TAB tape.

the direction of each of the perforations and in the direction that the tape is moving. In addition, the tape's upper and lower sections are clamped.

In method 1, the structure is such that high temperatures of from 300 to 400° C are transmitted from the bottom of the IC to the tape. This heat causes the tape to warp.

In method 2, because the tape is in reel form during shipping and conveyance, there are kinks that form and obstruct movement in the winding direction. Because of differences in each tape's structure, kinks are also formed that obstruct sprocket-to-sprocket movement.

In method 1, the tape fixation is by means of absorption and clamping only. Because of the loosening caused by tape warpage and undulation, however, force sufficient for adequate fixation is not obtained. To solve this problem, tension must be applied to the tape as in method 2. It is necessary to maintain the planarization of the tape surface and the leads.

CONCLUSION

We developed SP-TAB-ILB equipment and investigated its applicability to the TCP mounting of large-scale, narrow-pin-pitch ICs. As a sample we used a 16 mm^2, 608 pin, 90-μm pitch IC.

For this sample, specific bonding conditions must be met to insure appropriate initial bonding strength and bond conditions. These are bonding temperature of 350 to 400° C, ultrasonic power of 0.25 to 0.30 W, bonding load of 50 to 80 gf/lead, bonding time of 30 ms, and lead plating thickness of 0.5 to 1.0 μm. Results obtained under these conditions were an initial bonding strength of greater than 20 gf and a lead break percentage of greater than 85%.

For the SP-TAB-ILB of large-scale, high-pin-count, narrow-pitch ICs, it is desirable to first bond the pads at the four corners of the IC in a sequence of opposite corners, and then to bond the rest of the pads.

In SP-TAB-ILB, it is necessary to maintain the planarization of the tape surface and leads by applying tension to the tape. The establishment of low temperature bonding technology, transfer bump bonding technology, bonding technology for tin-plated leads, the investigation of TAB tape tools suitable for SP-TAB-ILB, and the establishment of high precision SP-TAB-ILB technology are issues that remain to be addressed.

REFERENCES

[1] T. Nemoto et al., "A feasibility study on single point TAB for high lead counts and fine pitch LSI," *Proc. 1990 IMC,* pp. 202–207, May 1990.

[2] K. Atsumi et al., "Inner lead bonding techniques for 500-lead dies having a 90 μm lead pitch," *Proc. 1990 ECC,* pp. 171–176, May 1989.

[3] Tsujimura, *Single Point Electro Packaging Technology,* pp. 53–56, July 1989.

Inspection and Evaluation after Inner Lead Bonding

Kenzo Hatada

Matsushita Electric Industrial Co., Ltd.,
Semiconductor Research Center

INTRODUCTION

In the inspection and evaluation after inner lead bonding (ILB), both the materials for the tape and bumps as well as the equipment used for bonding them are evaluated. Inspection and evaluation are also carried out because the results have to be fed back to materials, equipment, and process parameters.

In bonding of tape leads and bumps, gold, tin, or solder is used for plating the leads and for the bump materials. Thus, as many bonding conditions exist as combinations of these materials.

General inspection of bonds includes the pull test for inner leads and the shear strength test for bumps that are bonded to inner leads. Because only bonding results are evaluated in these tests, visual tests (e.g., scanning electron microscopy) of bonds and leads is important.

Because materials, equipment, and processes are integrated in the evaluation after inner lead bonding, analytical capability is required to examine the results of evaluation in detail.

INSPECTION AND EVALUATION AFTER INNER LEAD BONDING

Inspection after inner lead bonding includes strength tests for leads and bumps, and visual tests to observe the condition of bonds. Bonds are evaluated on the basis of these two types of tests.

Strength Tests

Strength tests after inner lead bonding include the pull test for inner leads and the shear strength test for bumps. A strength tester as shown in Fig. 1 is usually used for both tests.

When a lead pull test is carried out, a sample used for the test is cut from the tape on which a die is bonded and fixed on a glass slide with double-sided tape (Fig. 2). A hook for the pull test is inserted in the space between the die and the ILB window. The hook is pulled upward at a uniform rate, and the shear strength of the lead and the failure mode are measured.

In a lead pull test, because the bump strength is greater than the shear strength of the lead, the leads break in most cases. If the bump itself peels in this test, re-investigation of the bumping process is required.

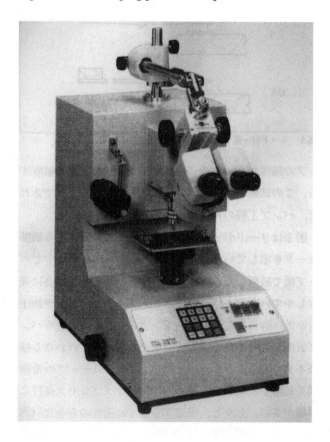

Fig. 1   Strength tester. (Lesca PRT-01)

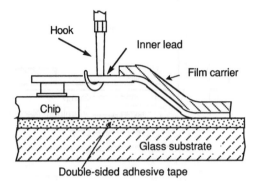

Fig. 2 Lead pull test method.

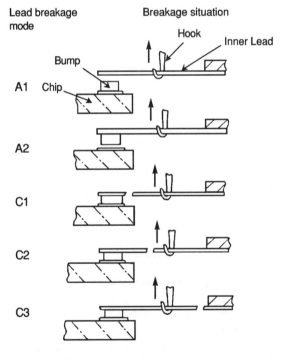

Fig. 3 Lead pull test breakage modes.

Figure 3 shows failure modes which occur during the lead pull test. In mode A1, the inner lead and the bump are separated. This mode tends to occur when bonding conditions are imperfect. For example, mode A1 occurs when the temperature of the thermode or the force is low or when the surface of the inner

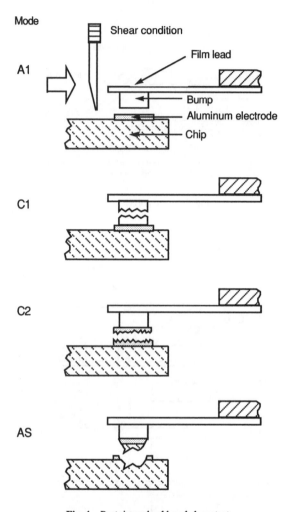

Fig. 4 Post–inner lead bond shear test.

lead or the bump is contaminated. In mode A2, the bump and the bonding pad of the die are separated. In most cases, this mode results from problems with parameters for the bumping process. However, as discussed later, it also occurs when excessive alloying (gold–tin eutectic alloy, for example) results in Au diffusion into the lead. Both cases are examples of defective bonds. Modes C1, C2, and C3 are desirable lead break modes. In mode C1, the lead is broken near the bump. This mode usually occurs when a large amount of a gold–tin alloy (where the lead is tin plated) is formed in the area where the lead breaks. The gold–tin alloy hardens the lead itself, resulting in loss of flexibility. In mode C2, the lead breaks in the middle. This is the most desirable of the C modes. In mode C3, the lead breaks near the ILB window. This mode usually occurs when the inner lead is relatively long.

The pull test for inner leads is a standard for judging the integrity of bonds. If a mode is obtained in a test in which the lead itself breaks, high reliability can be expected. When detailed data are required, bonds are analyzed and evaluated by recording the values and modes of the pull strength test. Modes C1 and C2 sometimes vary slightly, depending on the position of the lead at which the hook is set or the direction in which the hook is pulled. The lead pull test is evaluated as a production sampling test during the bonding process whereas the shear strength test is evaluated when the bonding parameters are set.

Figure 4 shows failure modes of the shear strength test. The shear strength test after inner lead bonding is the same as that during bump inspection. Shear strength is evaluated after bonding because the change in the bond strength of the bump due to the temperature and force, which are applied during bonding, is evaluated. If the bump shear strength is low after the bump is formed, the strength sometimes further deteriorates after bonding. In addition, cracks sometimes occur in silicon dioxide underneath the aluminum bonding pad or in silicon that was not present during bump formation. In such cases cracks in the surface of silicon dioxide and silicon can be observed by removing the metal film (i.e., the bump and the aluminum bonding pad) with aqua regia after bonding.

Mode A1 in Fig. 4 is a failure mode in which the bump and the aluminum bonding pad are separated. In mode C1, the bump itself breaks. In mode C2, the aluminum bonding pad breaks. Both of these modes are desirable. In mode AS, cracks occur in silicon and silicon dioxide of the die. This is an extremely undesirable mode.

In general, both the lead pull test and the shear strength test are conducted on all leads and bumps of a die. What degree materials, equipment, and processes are attributable is analyzed by evaluating the modes and strength that are obtained within a die.

Visual Tests

Visual tests are important in confirming the results that are evaluated in strength tests. In visual tests, the degree of the bond, the degree of the damage to the die, and the degree of the contact with the lead are all evaluated.

Figure 5 shows ideal bonds after inner lead bonding. In Fig. 5, the formation of an ideal gold–tin eutectic alloy is observed between tin-plated leads and gold bumps. An especially important point in bonds made by gold–tin eutectic alloy is that the plating thickness of leads and the bump thickness are controlled so as not to form excessive eutectic alloy.

Fig. 5   Good inner lead bond condition.

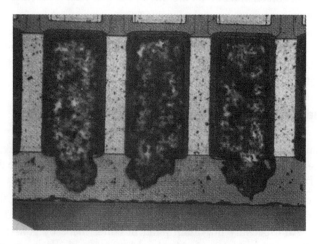

Fig. 6   Bump after etching has been removed from the leads. Excessive eutectic alloy can be observed.

Figure 6 is an example in which excessive eutectic alloy is formed. When the bump surface is observed by removing the inner lead, a large amount of a eutectic alloy is formed in the direction of the edge of the die. The eutectic alloy causes shorting of the bump and the edge of the die and induces electrical failure. If the eutectic alloy touches the surface of the die, it causes cracks in the silicon dioxide and induces electrical failure. Approximately 0.4 microns is desirable for tin-plating thickness on the lead. When the lead is gold-plated and the bump consists of gold, such failures do not occur. But because the temperature and force during bonding is high in gold–gold thermocompression bonding, cracks sometimes occur in silicon dioxide underneath the bonding pad or silicon.

Figure 7 shows an example in which the gold of the bump is diffused into the lead and the contact area of the bump is reduced. This occurs when the gold bump is not thick enough or when the tin-plating on the lead is too thick. In such conditions, because a part of the gold bump disappears, the shear strength of the bump tends to deteriorate. In the evaluation of the bond, observation by scanning

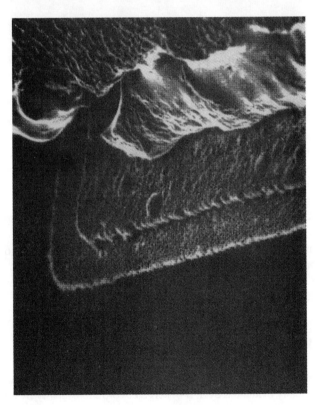

Fig. 7   The bump's gold has been drawn to the sides of the leads.

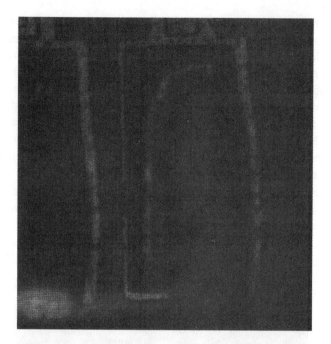

Fig. 8 Bump deformation generated during inner lead bonding.

electron microscopy can grasp the actual state more easily than observation by a metallurgical microscope.

Too much deformation of the bump is a mode that occurs frequently during volume production (Fig. 8). When the lead is oxidized or the bump surface is contaminated, the force and temperature are increased during bonding because the bonding strength deteriorates. As a result, the lead presses and spreads the bump itself, which causes the aluminum bonding pad to slip sideways and the passivation around the bonding pad to get damaged.

When the corresponding position of the die and the tape is not adequate during bonding, shorting of the bonded lead and the edge of the die sometimes occurs. By observing the cross-section of the die, the forming of the inner lead can be evaluated. Figure 9 shows ideal inner lead forming.

FUTURE ISSUES AND PROSPECTS

Inspection of inner lead bonding includes destructive tests because the bond cannot be electrically evaluated even if observed two-dimensionally by a metallurgical microscope. Because the tape and the bumps vary depending on the lot, the

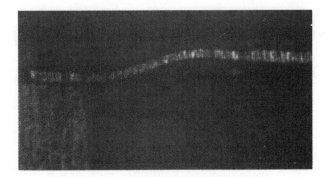

Fig. 9 Ideal inner lead forming.

bonds, in turn, vary accordingly. While TAB is gang bonding, inspection and evaluation techniques are based on a single part. If materials can be controlled with high precision, the inspection of inner lead bonding is expected to be as easy as the inspection of wire bonding. Improvements in materials are awaited.

Post–Outer Lead Bonding Inspection and Evaluation

Kenzo Hatada

Matsushita Electric Industrial Co., Ltd.
Semiconductor Research Center

INTRODUCTION

Almost all of the widely used small outline packages (SOP) and quad flat package (QFP) semiconductor packages use soldering for lead connection. For tape automated bonding (TAB) packages, however, there are a number of different methods used for outer lead bonding. At present, the method depends upon the device being bonded. Thus, there is no fixed method of inspection and evaluation following the outer lead bonding.

Figure 1 shows outer lead bonding methods used for TAB packages. Figure 1a shows a method in which solder connects the outer leads and the circuit board. This method has been used for a long time to bond TAB package leads. It is mainly used for connecting modules to glass epoxy or ceramic substrates. The solder material is applied to either the circuit board or the leads and a thermode heater or a pulse tool is used to melt the solder. Figure 1b and c illustrate methods widely used for liquid crystal display modules. In method b, a liquid or sheet consisting of thermoplastic or thermosetting resin and dispersed metallic particles such as nickel or solder is placed between the outer leads and the circuit board. Heat is then applied to form the connection. In method c, an optically hardening insulating resin is placed between the outer leads and the circuit board. While pressure is applied, ultraviolet illumination hardens the resin and forms the connection.

It is conjectured that more than half of all TAB packages use either method b or c. There is little published information from the companies involved, but the types of inspection and evaluation that take place after bonding is as follows:

1. external inspection (bridges between leads),

2. electrical inspection (connection resistance, frequency characteristics), and

3. bond strength inspection.

When the bonding method shown in Fig. 1a is used, the main inspections and evaluations performed are external inspection and bond strength inspection. When methods b or c are used, electrical and connection strength inspection are mainly performed.

Evaluation methods are not standardized for the inspection methods used for each bonding method. Conditions vary slightly for each device and from company to company. This is probably due to the fact that TAB outer lead bonding is still under development.

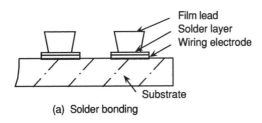

Film lead
Solder layer
Wiring electrode
Substrate

(a) Solder bonding

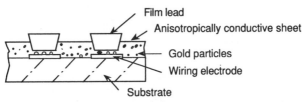

Film lead
Anisotropically conductive sheet
Gold particles
Wiring electrode
Substrate

(b) Anisotropically conductive sheet bonding

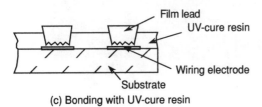

Film lead
UV-cure resin
Wiring electrode
Substrate

(c) Bonding with UV-cure resin

Fig. 1 The types of outer lead bonding methods.

POST–OUTER LEAD BONDING INSPECTION AND EVALUATION

There are three types of inspection and evaluation after TAB outer lead bonding. These are 1) external inspection and evaluation by means of a microscope to ascertain the bonding condition, 2) electrical inspection and evaluation to measure the connection resistance of the bond sections and crosstalk, and 3) bond strength inspection and evaluation to measure the outer lead bond strength (mainly peel strength).

Evaluation with Visual Inspection

Almost all applications of the visual inspection of bonds involve bonding methods that use soldering. The inspection method is the same as for QFP, SOP, and other types of packages. Commercially available visual inspection equipment (Fig. 2) can be used. At present, there are few examples of large numbers of TAB devices being mounted on the same circuit board. Rather, the present situation is that QFPs and other commonly used packages are mounted in large numbers, with only a few TAB packages among them. Moreover, because bonding methods for existing packages are basically different from the bonding methods used for

Fig. 2   Lead external inspection equipment (Kyushu Matsushita Electric VC10C-S).

TAB packages, in most cases only the TAB packages are specially inspected and evaluated using a microscope.

Special inspection may be required due to instability in the bond between the lead (which may use a variety of outer lead platings including tin, gold, and solder) and the electrode material on the circuit board. Visual inspection is rarely performed for methods b and c in Fig. 1, which use either an anisotropic conductive sheet or UV-cure resin (mostly used for liquid crystal display modules).

Evaluation with Electrical Inspection

The connection resistance is measured when bonding methods b and c in Fig. 1 are used, but not all of the modules are measured. Connection resistance is measured when bonding conditions are set. This is because bonding methods b and c utilize the adherence of the resin. Moreover, because the circuit board used is a glass substrate and the electrode materials also use indium tin oxide film, which is difficult to solder, it is easy for the absolute value of the connection's resistance and its variation in width to grow large.

The four-terminal method is a commonly used electrical inspection method. Because the dispersed metal particles in Fig. 1b cause signal leakage (crosstalk) between adjacent leads, in some cases the frequency dependence of the crosstalk is measured and the interconnection materials and conditions are evaluated. These measurements are made for narrow-pitch or high frequency devices when conditions are initially set.

Evaluation with Bonding Strength Inspection

Bonding strength inspection is performed no matter what the connection method. In general, the inspection methods used are the lead pull strength test and the peel strength test (Fig. 3). In the lead pull strength test, the outer leads bonded to the circuit board's electrodes are pulled to determine the outer lead's break strength and break mode. The pull strength test method and break mode determination are almost exactly the same as those used after inner lead bonding. The same types of pull strength test equipment can be used.

On the other hand, peel strength tests are often used for TAB package outer lead bond evaluation. As shown in Fig. 3b, the outer leads bonded to the circuit board are pulled vertically and the lead's tearing strength is measured. This is an especially important evaluation as the outer lead pitch becomes narrow. In solder connection methods, because the connection between the circuit board electrodes and the outer leads is formed with the addition of pressure, the solder materials do not completely cover the outer leads. The connection is only between the solder and the sides of the outer leads. For this reason the peel strength value is unexpectedly low.

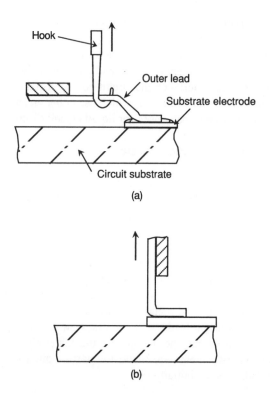

Fig. 3   Bond strength test.

Evaluation with Other Types of Inspection

One item must be included in post–outer lead bonding evaluation that is not evaluation of the bonds. As shown in Fig. 4, the outer leads are formed when they are mounted onto the circuit board. This is done to absorb the thermal coefficient of expansion of the large scale integration (LSI) chip and the circuit board and to correct the height difference between the circuit board and the chip. However, if the lead is formed incorrectly (the lead bend rate is not correct), cracks will form where the lead bends, reducing the long-term reliability of the connection.

Figure 5 shows cracks generated during outer lead forming. A number of cracks can be seen running in the lead's vertical direction. This type of phenomenon is easily generated in tin-plated leads and gold-plated leads with a nickel sublayer exposed to the relatively high temperatures such as with burn-in testing. It is conjectured that the tin-plated leads crack because of the formation of a hard copper–tin alloy, while the gold-plated leads crack because of the interposition of the

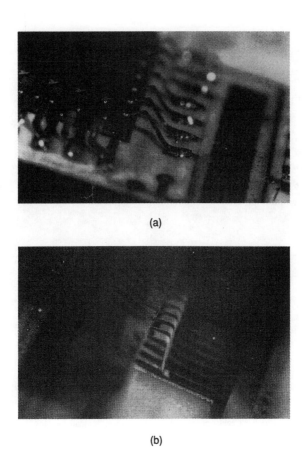

(a)

(b)

Fig. 4 Outer lead bonding condition.

hard nickel material. As seen in Fig. 6, these cracks expand during thermal shock and heat cycle tests and eventually cause lead breaks.

It is necessary to inspect for cracks with a scanning electron microscope (SEM) to observe and evaluate the relationship between the amount of outer lead forming (i.e., bend rate) and reliability. The microcracks produced during lead forming will appear in the final step as lead breaks. It is often the case that marketed products become defective because cracks occur in the plating on the copper leads, exposing the copper, and accelerating its corrosion, eventually resulting in lead breaks.

SEM observation is optimal for microcrack detection. One preventive measure is to optimize the amount of lead forming. Microcracking also depends heavily on the precision and thoroughness (i.e., completeness) of the metal molds.

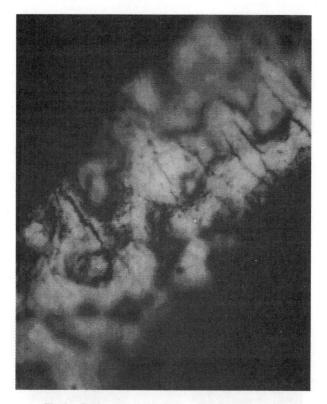

Fig. 5 Cracks generated in leads, caused by lead forming.

ISSUES AND PROSPECTS

The difficulty of post–outer lead inspection and evaluation will increase as a result of three factors. First, the TAB package itself will have narrower pitch (below 100 μm pitch) and higher pin counts. Second, there is a possibility that bonding methods will diversify. Bonding methods are not limited to soldering as with QFP and SOP packages. Third, companies are doing a number of things with TAB packages, such as folding them over, and using packages of different sizes and shape. The problem is what type of inspection and evaluation technology should be used to meet these three issues. There are many manufacturers that have been using TAB packages for some time, but most of these manufacturers only perform inspection and evaluation when they set the conditions, and perform few inspections and evaluations during the mass production process. The inspections that are being performed are done with microscopes.

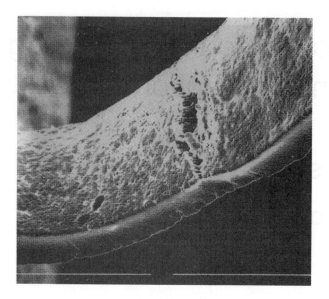

Fig. 6   A lead in break condition.

TAB technology is an emerging technology. There are many essential areas where progress must be made in terms of materials, equipment, and processes. It is natural to hope that inspection and evaluation technology will develop to an even higher level.

Introducing TAB Technology to the Production Site

Akira Suzuki

Casio Computer Co., Ltd.

INTRODUCTION

Tape automated bonding (TAB) technology is attracting much attention as a large scale integration (LSI) package technology well suited to thin, high-pin-count packages. The shift from plastic molded quad flat packages (QFPs), which have been the mainstream package in wire bonding, to TAB packages (or tape carrier packages, TCP) is proceeding rapidly. Recently, TAB technology is becoming particularly active in the office automation field in the form of thin, high-pin-count LSI drivers for flat panel displays. This paper describes the technical aspects and considerations we faced as a systems house in introducing TAB technology at the production level.

CHARACTERISTICS OF TAB

In progressively replacing QFPs, TAB technology offers some superior characteristics. Table 1 provides an overview of these characteristics, comparing TAB to a thin small outline package (TSOP). Several of the key characteristics are summarized below.

　　1. The best characteristic is that TAB lends itself to thin, high-pin-count packages. At less than 1-mm thick, TCP breaks the 200-pin limit of molded packages like TSOPs and QFPs. True, TSOPs can be as thin as 1 mm, but many prob-

TABLE 1   Comparison of Packages for LCD Application

Items compared	TAB packages (TCP)	Flat packages (TSOP)
Structure		
Thin	<1 mm thick possible	Max. 1 mm thick
High pin count	200–500 pins	20–100 pins
Shape	Bendable	Not bendable
Materials		
LSI chips	Bump required	Bump not required
Substrate	Tape carrier	Lead frame
Bond material	Inner lead	Gold wire
Encapsulation resin	Potting material	Molding material
Bonding method		
ILB	Gang bonding	Wire bonding
OLB	Solder, anisotropic paste	Solder
Assembly		
Mountability	Good	Fair
Cost	Good	Fair
Reliability	Good	Fair

lems remain with their high cost, usage restrictions (such as reflow), and difficulty in handling high pin counts.

2. Because LSIs can be mounted onto TAB tape in a continuous process, it is especially suited to mass production of a single product by means of continuous roll-to-roll automated processing on tape lengths of 50 to 100 m. Thus it is used in high quantities in the assembly of watches and calculators. Promoting ever thinner and lighter packages, TAB also contributes to lower costs.

3. The tape package is very flexible and can dramatically reduce mounting areas by being folded over. While recent flat panel displays have grown larger, as shown in Fig. 1, the mounting area can be reduced by designing the LSI driver as a TAB package that can be folded 90° or 180°.

4. Multiple LSI chips can be placed on a single tape to make multichip or hybrid packages, thereby increasing placement efficiency and functionality. This method is, in fact, used in multifunction watches and high-pin-count drivers for flat panel displays.

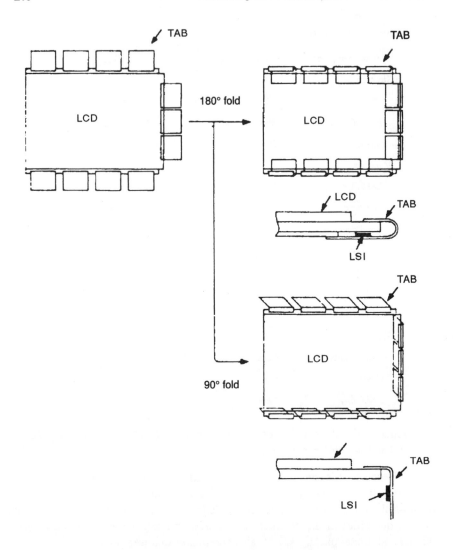

Fig. 1   Folded TAB packages in liquid crystal displays.

TRENDS IN TAB-RELATED INDUSTRIES

TAB production quantities tend to increase each year as shown in Table 2. The structure of the Japanese TAB industry, shown in Fig. 2, is divided into five groups: base materials suppliers, materials suppliers, semiconductor suppliers, assembly suppliers, and systems houses.

Semiconductor makers were at one time pessimistic about the introduction of TAB, but have since become the technological leaders and are attentive to technologic development trends. Large semiconductor makers in particular are now in a position of leadership in relation to makers of raw and other materials and are establishing TAB technology groups with their own technology as the core.

The TAB technology groups of major semiconductor makers have actively begun developing and improving bump formation technology, the final process in fabricating wafers, and are putting forth every effort in developing thin, high-pin-count packages (see Table 3). Nevertheless, bump formation technology has yet to establish itself as a mature wafer process technology. In particular, because many LSIs being assembled into TAB packages are existing LSIs that are not specially designed for TAB, the current situation is that aspects such as final passivation, electrode arrangement, and reliability have yet to be optimized.

In terms of technology and mass production capability, specialized tape suppliers have reached a high level and are now pulling the tape material and copper material suppliers along. For the present, the major issues are fine patterns (100 to 80 μm pitch pattern), tape cost reduction, and increasing the tape width from 35 mm to 70 mm to 140 mm. As for tape base material, polyimide is the material of choice and is available in either Kapton® and Upilex® brands. Development trends that may reduce the cost of the base material are always of interest.

In most cases, bonding the LSI chip to the tape carrier is done in-house by the semiconductor maker; rarely is it done by the user. This is probably because TAB is a form of semiconductor package and in terms of control of quality and reliability, it is natural to do the packaging in-house. Recently, however, systems

TABLE 2 TAB Production (Based on Tape Production)

	◄——— Actual ———►			◄——— Predicted ———►		
	1987	1988	1989	1990	1991	1992
Volume (km)*						
≥150 pins	210	2,150	3,600	7,160	8,100	10,830
≤149 pins	2,550	3,850	4,200	4,840	6,300	7,170
Total	2,760	6,000	7,800	12,000	14,400	18,000
Value (millions of yen)						
≥150 pins	850	1,350	2,300	2,960	4,200	5,630
≤149 pins	2,550	3,850	4,200	4,840	6,300	7,170
Total	3,400	5,200	6,500	7,800	10,500	12,800

Source: FKI, *TAB Market Trends and Forecast 1990*
*Calculated for 35 mm width

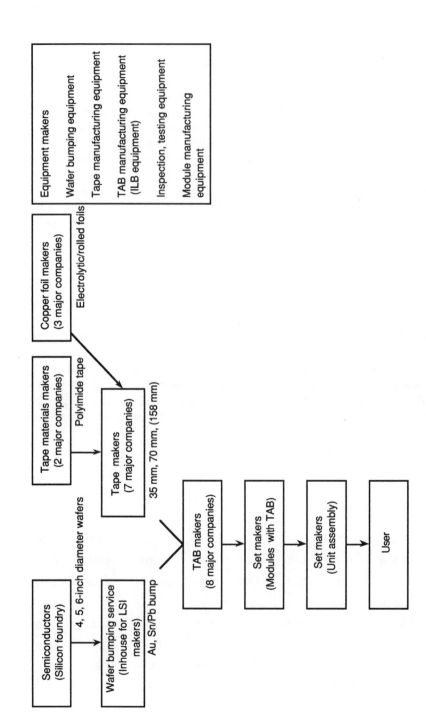

Fig. 2 TAB industry structure.

TABLE 3 Straight Bump Developments of Semiconductor Suppliers

	Toshiba	Hitachi	NEC	Mitsubishi	Fujitsu
Barrier metal	Ti/Ni	—	Ti/Pt	Cr/Cu	Ti/TiPd
Bump material	Au	Au	Au	Au	Au
Allowable height variance	±2 μm	—	±5 μm	±3 μm	±3 μm
Required ILB pitch	—	100 μm	100 μm	120 μm	100 μm
Height limit	—	—	20 μm	25 μm	50 μm
Resist method	Double coated film	Single coated	Thick film resist	Single coated	—

	Matsushita	Oki Electric	Sharp	Epson	Rohm	TI Japan
Barrier metal	Ti/Pd	Ti/Pt	TiW/TiW	—	—	TiW/Au
Bump material	Au	Au	Au	Au, solder	Au	Au
Allowable height variance	±0.5 μm	±7 μm	±2 μm	±5 μm	±1 μm	±1.5 μm
Required ILB pitch	80 μm	80 μm	90 μm	100 to 120 μm	60 μm	100 μm
Height limit	20 μm	—	20 μm	—	—	20 μm
Resist method	—	—	Single coated	—	—	—

Source: Nikkei Microdevices (February 1990)

TABLE 4   Main Equipment Required for TAB Production

	Process outline	Equipment	Equipment cost (100 million yen)
Tape carrier	Punching	Press equipment	0.3
	Laminate	Laminating equipment	0.2
	Resist pattern	Resist processing equipment	1.0
		Exposure equipment	0.5
	Etching	Etching equipment	0.5
	Plating	Plating equipment	0.6
	Pattern Inspection	External inspection equipment	0.7
Bumped electrode	UBM	Vaporization, sputter equipment	1.0
	Resist	Resist processing equipment	0.5
		Mask aligner	0.7
	Plating	Plating Equipment	0.5
	Etching	Etching equipment	1.0
	Bump inspection	External inspection equipment	0.2
TAB	Dicing	Dicing equipment	0.3
	ILB	Inner lead bonder	0.5
	Encapsulation	Encapsulation equipment	0.4
	Function inspection	TAB handler	0.3
		LSI tester	0.4
	Excising	Press equipment	0.4

Note: The cost of the frame carrier and the TAB related equipment depends on the width of the tape. The figures in this table are based on costs for tape wider than 70 mm.

houses have made inroads into this field and are changing the utilization of semiconductors. They are introducing TAB manufacturing techniques in order to increase their freedom in producing assemblies and to lower packaging costs by purchasing bare chip LSIs or unpackaged wafers. In the future, some system makers will probably expand this operation for external sales.

Along with these developments, equipment manufacturers are also engaged in brisk development. Assembly equipment manufacturers in particular, who have focused on wire bonding in the past, are now vigorously announcing new TAB-related equipment. Until now, TAB equipment has been scarce, consisting of machines mostly developed independently by users and introduced into their own production site. With the emergence of specialized equipment manufacturers, however, low-cost, highly functional equipment is beginning to appear. Table 4 shows the main types of equipment required for TAB production.

PROBLEMS IN INTRODUCING TAB

TCP manufacturing technology consists of the basic technologies shown in Fig. 3. Discussed below are tips and problems related to each of the technologies when developing production techniques.

TAB Package Design

It is important that TAB package designs be optimized with the final assembly image in mind. Figure 4 depicts the TAB design flow with a summary of each stage. It begins with design of the LSI, then progresses through bump design, tape carrier design, inner lead bonding (ILB) design, outer lead bonding (OLB) design, circuit design, and test design, with each design step interrelated to the others. TAB packages are fabricated by following these basic design specifications.

Taking the TAB design of an LSI driver for a liquid crystal display as an example, this paper will explain the main points of each of the design techniques. The LSI driver shown in Fig. 5 is divided into input terminals and output terminals. The output terminals outnumber the input terminals. In a standard design, arranging the output terminals along three sides of the LSI chip with the remaining side for input terminals makes the TAB design or module placing design easier.

In bump design, optimal sizes are determined from the aluminum pad size and overcoat size, as shown in Fig. 6. The bump height differs according to the ILB conditions, but to prevent edge joints in the leads, heights of 20 to 25 μm are often used. Straight bumps are used as the bump shape to support fine pitches (see Fig. 7).

The shape of the tape carrier differs according to whether or not the tape is folded over. If the tape is to be folded, the design of the slits is critical. Inner lead shape and dimensions are determined during bump design, but the shape must be designed while taking into consideration the characteristics of the copper materials used. Also, it is important to design the layout of test pads for checking the electrical characteristics of the final LSI package, creating a layout and pattern shape that allows accurate probing at the tape surface (see Fig. 8). The preparatory design for production is completed with ILB and OLB design for interconnecting the package, and the test probe design.

Problems in TAB Production

To make LSI chips into TAB packages the bump process is placed as the final process in the LSI wafer process, but the importance of this process is not well recognized. It can be said that this process makes or breaks bond quality and

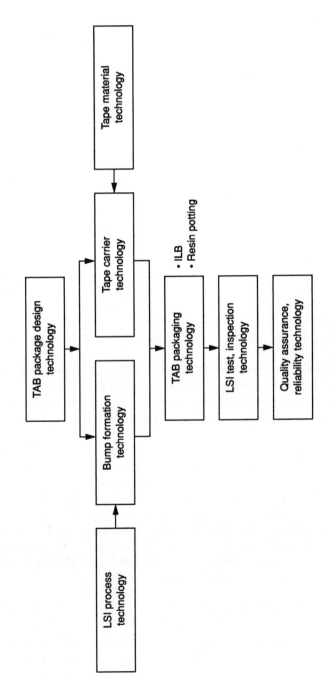

Fig. 3 Manufacturing technology for TAB packages.

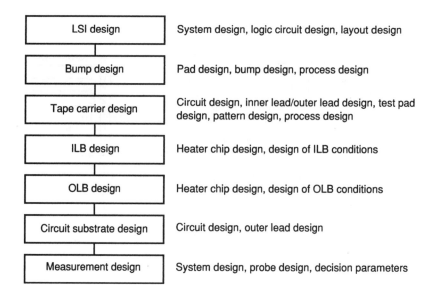

Fig. 4   Design outline of TAB technology.

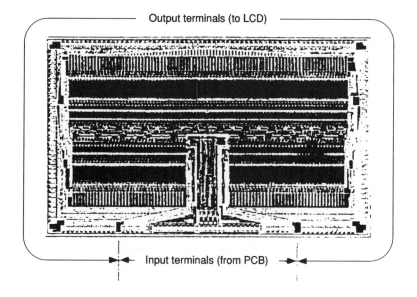

Fig. 5   Liquid crystal display driver LSI.

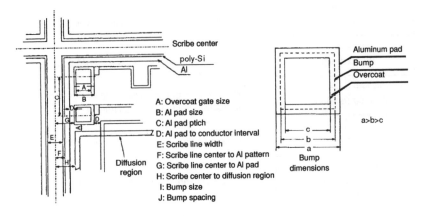

Fig. 6   Example of bump design.

reliability, and requires minimizing variations in dimensions and characteristics in production.

Obtaining LSI. From the viewpoint of the assembly maker or systems house that is not manufacturing LSI chips, it is possible to obtain bumped die. However, the type and quantity are limited and the cost of the bumping process is high. In fact, 20 to 30% of the cost of a standard bumped chip are the costs of bumping. As a result, in some cases a foundry method has been implemented, in which bumps are fabricated in-house to reduce costs as well as to expand TAB applications beyond customized chips.

Wafer Size. Although the main wafer size currently in use is 5 inches in diameter, LSI drivers for liquid crystal displays are fabricated on 4-inch wafers, while dynamic RAM and static RAM memories and customized LSIs for calculators and watches use 6-inch wafers. While the current bump process technology can accommodate wafers as large as 6 inches in diameter, a flexible bump process line capable of supporting 4, 5, and 6-inch diameter wafers is greatly needed. If the basic line is set up to handle 6-inch wafers but capable of switching to 4 or 5-inch wafers, the line could be used closer to full capacity.

Bump Process Yield. As the last process in fabricating the wafer, the bump process must show high yields, and in particular must prevent changes in characteristics during the process. Recently, electrodeposition, sputtering, and dry etching have come into use and care must be taken to avoid electron beam damage or ion damage. On this point, work is needed in optimizing the final passivation

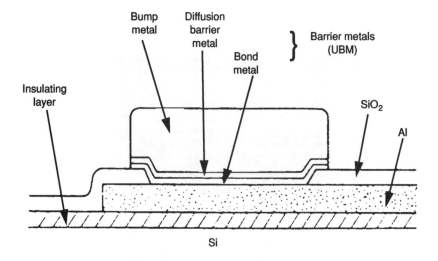

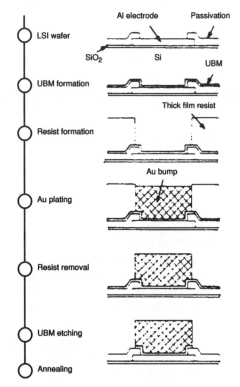

Fig. 7 Straight bump.

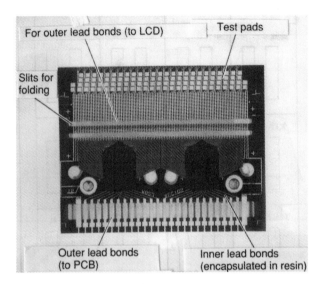

For outer lead bonds (to LCD)   Test pads

Slits for folding

Outer lead bonds (to PCB)   Inner lead bonds (encapsulated in resin)

Fig. 8   Inner and outer lead bond sites for TAB tape carrier package.

film that is suited to the bump process. Provided that there is no damage to the wafer at the bump process, a design able to give 95% or greater yields is needed.

To obtain high yields in the production of tape carriers, automation of equipment capable of "roll-to-roll" (Casio's variation of reel-to-reel) processing is needed. The tape carrier is mostly produced to the user's specifications; standard tape carrier just does not exist. For this reason there is great variation among user specifications in the pattern design and selection of materials and, as a result, yields change greatly according to the specification, making costs vary greatly.

Selection of Tape Width. Moving up from 35 mm, tape widths of 70 mm or 140 mm (actually 158 mm) are coming into use to raise production efficiency and to support ever larger TAB patterns or multiple chips. Which tape widths are to be employed depends on the required functionality, size, and quantity of the TAB package. But present manufacturing equipment itself does not flexibly support differing tape widths so the selection must be made carefully.

Testing the Tape Carrier Pattern. The present bottleneck in fabricating the tape carrier is the testing process for checking the pattern and other features. Along with the move toward ever-finer and ever-larger TAB patterns comes the need for automated pattern inspection equipment that employs vision processing techniques to carry out checks that have, in the past, been done with the naked eye. Good results from tests by automated equipment exist for fine pattern tests, photomask defect tests, wafer pattern defect tests, and board circuit pattern tests. However, equipment for inspecting long, flexible substrates like a tape carrier are still in the developmental stage. A representative example of a defective pattern is shown in Fig. 9.

The manufacturing processes of TAB packages involve gang bonding the bumped LSI chip to the inner leads on the tape carrier by thermocompression bonding, then covering the chip and inner lead bonds with a resin potting. To

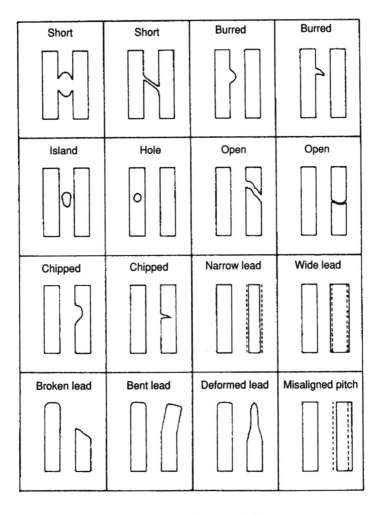

Fig. 9 Representative pattern defects.

TABLE 5   Process Technology Issues

TAB processes and technological issues

Wafer bumping
1. Wafer availability
2. Wafer size selection
3. Straight bump process development
4. Process automation
5. Test probe for bumps
6. Yield improvement

Tape carrier
1. Tape width selection
2. Decreasing material costs
3. Pattern inspection automation
4. Process automation
5. Improved pattern pitch precision
6. Plating stabilization
7. Yield improvement
8. Multilayer tape development

ILB
1. Adaptability to large LSI chips
2. Improved placement precision
3. Different types of multichip bonding
4. Compatibility with increased tape width
5. Improved throughput

Test
1. Improved probing precision
2. Compatibility with higher pin counts
3. Decreased test costs
4. Burn-in test
5. Reliability evaluation

raise yields and improve ease of production, automated equipment capable of handling roll-to-roll tape supply is needed. ILB equipment and resin potting equipment are representative examples. ILB equipment aligns the bump electrode on the LSI chip to the lead areas on the tape carrier and bonds the two by thermocompression. Because repair is impossible after potting, the equipment must be capable of precision alignment.

After potting comes the functional testing of the LSI chip, where all points are tested by a TAB automated handler. Because the test probe must accurately meet with the tape's test pads, contact is made by a probe card method. The LSI chip is checked according to a prepared test pattern and final yields are determined. Tables 5 and 6 summarize the technological tasks of the TAB processes along with some points relative to introducing TAB to the production site.

TABLE 6   Key Points for Introducing TAB Production

Obtain required materials (external supply or internal manufacture)	
1. LSI (wafer or bumped bare chips)	
2. Tape carrier	
3. OLB bond materials	
Introduction of mass production equipment	Equipment cost outline*
1. Bump process equipment	400 to 500 million yen
2. Tape carrier manufacturing equipment	700 to 800 million yen
3. TAB manufacturing equipment	500 to 600 million yen
4. Testing equipment	300 to 400 million yen
5. Reliability evaluation equipment	<u>100 to 200 million yen</u>
	Total 2 to 2.5 billion yen
Mass Production line automation	
Roll-to-roll process	
Issues of quality, reliability and hermeticity	
Cost	
1. High yield, stable production	
2. Use of low cost materials	
3. Use of labor saving devices	

*Equipment costs presuppose a TAB production scale of 5 million units per month.

TAB APPLICATIONS

The use of TAB is expanding rapidly from calculators and watches into fields requiring functionality that can be supported only by TAB devices. Within these, it is safe to say that TAB is being applied most effectively in liquid crystal displays. In fact, pocket size televisions were made possible by TAB technology. Demand for TAB is quickly rising with its recent use in LCD drivers for personal computers and word processors. In addition, TAB is attracting a great deal of attention with its application in high capacity memory cards like 512 kilobit to 1 megabit static RAM cards.

References

[1] Suzuki, "Film Carrier and Bump Technology," *Semiconductor World,* pp. 113–125, June 1989.

[2] Suzuki, "Calculators: An Example in Introducing TAB," *Denshi Zairyo,* pp. 66–76, July 1989.

[3] Nakamura, "Using TAB in LSIs Outside of LCDs," *Nikkei Microdevices,* pp. 106–107, February 1990.

[4] Fuji Keizai, *TAB Market Trends and Predictions (II),* April 1990.

Part 5

Chip on Board Technology

Passivation Technology after COB Interconnect

Kenzo Hatada

Matsushita Electric Industrial Co., Ltd.
Semiconductor Research Center

INTRODUCTION

The most commonly used passivation method following chip on board (COB) mounting is resin application. Materials and types of passivation methods vary depending on the mounting method and reliability level required.

The purposes of passivation are to protect the large scale integration (LSI) chip, the bonding area, and bonding materials from exterior moisture, harmful chemicals, and mechanical and electrical damage. One type of passivation prevents electrode corrosion of the bonding material and bonding area due to moisture or oxidation under high temperature. Passivation of another type prevents chip damage due to human or mechanical contact directly on the LSI chip or lead. Such contact can cause static electricity damage or mechanical impact. The resin also prevents lead breakage and shorts caused by neighboring leads.

However strong the bonding or superb its electrical characteristics, lack of complete passivation after COB mounting renders the mounting defective. Passivation is thus the most important step for completing the mounted body and it affects the overall reliability of the component. When COB mounting is used with bare chips having thinner bodies, passivation becomes even more important.

SELECTION OF PASSIVATION RESIN

The important characteristics of a passivation resin are moisture resistance and a low coefficient of thermal expansion. Other characteristics, such as fluidity, thixotrophy, and productivity (including solvent content and setting temperature) are considered, but moisture resistance and low thermal expansion rate are the main factors to support large- and small-scale LSI chip production. Three types of resin show high resistance against moisture, as indicated in Fig. 1. Resin A readily allows moisture in and out. Silicone is one of these types with high purity. Even when the moisture seeps in easily, the water absorbed is of high purity and carries very few ions, so corrosion of the material is less likely to occur. The moisture escapes in a short time. Type A resins are widely used for the passivation of wire bonded chips, or inner and outer lead bondings (ILB/OLB) of TAB-mounted chips, being most commonly used for OLB of TAB-mounted chips. The silicone resin itself has pliability and is most appropriate for mechanically protecting the COB mounting.

Resin B does not allow moisture to seep in easily, yet once wet, the resin tenaciously retains the water. It is a time-consuming process to remove moisture from type B. Molding resin for semiconductor packages, such as epoxy with filler or silicon resin materials, belong to type B. When moisture remains within the package, expansion or cracking occurs.

Resin C allows moisture to enter fairly easily, yet it does not reach the surface of chip or bonding material because of the high adhesion rate between resin and chip or bonding material. Corrosion resistance is high with resin C, which is used mainly for TAB or wire bonding with thin resin film and high reliability. Resin C is based on a new concept.

Contraction in the resin during the setting can damage the mounted body. Resin should be selected to match the thermal expansion and stress tolerance of the LSI chip and bonding material. When the resin or setting conditions are selected incorrectly, defects as shown in Fig. 2 occur. Figure 2a and 2b illustrates wires broken by contraction of the protective resin. The inner wire may be broken as seen in Fig. 2a, or wires that extended from resin surface due to incomplete protection by the resin may be broken as seen in Fig. 2b. Soft silicone-type resin is used for the wire bonding method of COB mounting to avoid wire breakage. Figure 2c indicates the chip cracked due to the contraction force of the resin. To avoid these defects, resins with a low thermal coefficient should be used and, moreover, the heating during the setting and subsequent cooling should be gradual to produce as little internal stress as possible.

APPLICATION METHOD AND FORMS OF PASSIVATION RESIN

Application of resin and final forms of resin differ depending on the COB process mounting method. Figure 3 indicates the application method for wire bonding. Resin is dropped on the mounting area from a specialized nozzle. The resin

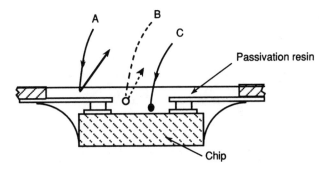

Fig. 1 Types of passivation resin.

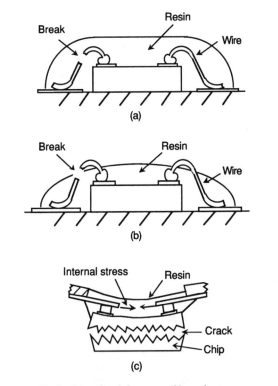

Fig. 2 Mounting defects caused by resin stress.

used in Fig. 3a is relatively clay-like and is used with larger mounting areas where resin overflow is allowed. With the method shown in Fig. 3b, sufficient resin is added to the resin mold to completely fill it. There are two types of molds; one is fastened on the substrate and the other is temporarily formed with a

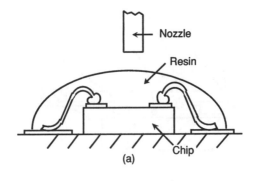

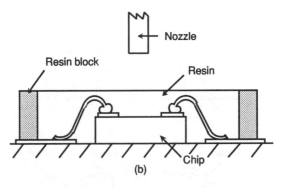

Fig. 3 Wire bonding resin sealing methods and shapes.

material such as rubber. The former uses material similar to the resin whereas the latter uses softer material such as silicone rubber that will not stick to the resin. The latter mold is removed after the resin has set. The permanent mold comes in two types; one is attached to the substrate while the other is printed directly on the substrate. When the printing method is used, the resin application area must be wider because the barrier is not high enough.

There are three types of resin application processes for TAB (Fig. 4). The whole chip is protected in Fig. 4a; resin with fiber is located on the reverse side of chip and resin is dripped from the chip surface for setting. The thickness of resin tends to be greater when this method is used. Resin is dripped only on the chip surface and bonding area in Fig. 4b. This process can protect either the chip surface or protect both the chip surface and the lead area. The thickness after the mounting is the thinnest when this method is used. A resin mold is used in case of Fig. 4c. The resin can be injected in the mold, which is made of either metal or with the method used in Fig. 3b. Recently, the latter is used more because of the wider selection range of available resins.

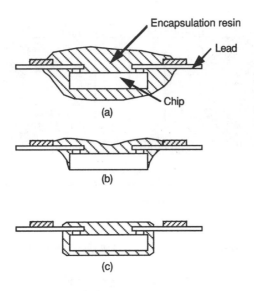

Fig. 4   TAB method resin coating formations.

COB mounting with TAB needs passivation not only on the ILB area but also on the OLB area. Figure 5 is an example of silicone resin applied on an OLB area. Silicone resin is applied on the whole TAB package. This prevents mechanical failure of the leads and shorts due to solder material left between the leads.

The resin application method for the ILB area consists of three methods as indicated in Fig. 6. In the stamp method, Fig. 6a, resin released from a hole in the stamp surface is transferred onto the chip surface. In Fig. 6b, a number of nozzles on the stamp surface allow resin to drip onto the assembly. The amount of resin can be controlled by changing the shape and number of nozzles. With the methods shown in Fig. 6a and 6b, stamps must be changed each time the size of the application area changes. In contrast, the nozzle etching method (Fig. 6c) can be adapted to any application surface area by controlling the speed of etching and using the appropriate amount of resin. This method is now used more frequently.

Figure 7 indicates the resin application method used for the flip chip process. The entire chip is covered by the resin. The purposes of resin application can be either to protect the bonding area from moisture or to support the mechanical feature. For flip chip bonding, passivation is performed for both.

PROBLEMS AND PROSPECTS

Passivation after the COB mounting requires various materials and application methods depending on the mounting technology and purposes. As for resin mate-

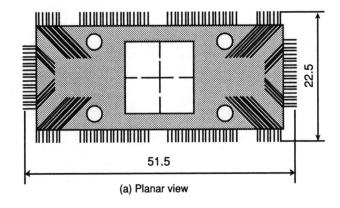

(a) Planar view

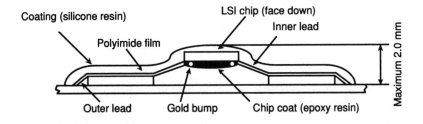

(b) Cross-section

Fig. 5   TAB method OLB preservation.

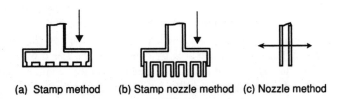

(a) Stamp method   (b) Stamp nozzle method   (c) Nozzle method

Fig. 6   Resin coating methods.

rials, there are type 1 and type 2 liquidity. Type 2 liquidity with solvent requires a venting facility and has different conditions for setting. The key factors to resin selection are low moisture and a low contraction force.

As COB becomes more widely used, the reliability standard also improves. The demand for better protective resins grows stronger. While a high level of reliability and low contraction force remain basic requirements, resin that can seep

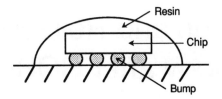

Fig. 7 Flip chip method resin coating formation.

through a few μm space and provide higher reliability in spite of thinness are new requirements.

In the future, passivation technology with thicknesses as low as a few thousand angstroms or so is desirable. The range of COB mounting technology is sure to be greater when thinner and more reliable passivation is possible.

Inspection and Reliability Technology after COB Interconnect

Kenzo Hatada

Matsushita Electric Industrial Co., Ltd.
Semiconductor Research Center

INTRODUCTION

Inspections after bare chips are mounted on the circuit substrate are quite difficult. Inspections include testing the electrical properties of the chip, bonding durability, and external inspection for faults such as floats and breakage of the leads. Most of the inspection executed after the chip on board (COB) mounting is concerned with electrical integrity; mounted chips proved defective are subjected to repair.

Certain mounting technologies, such as wire bonding and flip chip, do not allow for a complete electrical inspection before mounting on the substrate. The inclusion of a test electrode terminal where the chip is to be mounted allows for testing after the chip is mounted. By touching the inspection electrode, the electrical properties and chip quality can be determined. With tape automated bonding (TAB) technology, almost complete electrical inspection can be done before mounting, thus the inspection of the IC substrate as a whole is necessary.

The majority of bonding inspections check for breakage, testing the strength of the bond and breakage mode to judge the quality of the mounting process. During mass production, testing of only a few samples is common.

External inspection involves checking for breakage and float at the bonds, normally with microscopic inspection. It is impossible, however, to check all the details. Recently, external inspection has been replaced by preventive methods utilizing appropriate design of solder quantity and electrode measurement. The surface mount technology method of using large parts such as quad flat packages and small outline packages calls for the use of a specialized automated external inspection device.

For reliable inspection technology, conventional high temperature storage, high temperature and high humidity tests, and thermal shock tests are performed to evaluate electrical and other components. Testing for defects at an early stage is important because materials and structures are becoming much smaller.

INSPECTION TECHNOLOGY

Inspection technology consists of electrical, bonding, and external inspections. Electrical and external inspections are conducted indiscriminately, whereas bonding inspection is limited to breakage inspection only. The inspection technologies used for the COB mounting method are quite different than for other mounting methods. Figure 1 outlines electrical and external inspections undertaken during different mounting methods.

As with the wire bonding method, electric and external inspections are conducted after the chip is directly dye bonded or wire bonded onto the substrate.

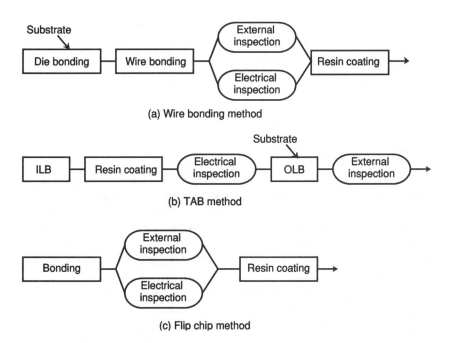

(a) Wire bonding method

(b) TAB method

(c) Flip chip method

Fig. 1 Inspection positioning for each chip on board mounting process.

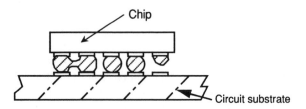

Fig. 2   Bonding defects in the flip chip method.

Wire breakage and chip stains can be checked visually while electrical inspection replaces external inspection. After the inspection, protective resin is applied to the wire portion.

The TAB method bonds a chip onto the TAB tape, inner lead bonding (ILB) is performed and, after resin is applied, electrical inspection and thickness of resin is checked using a probe card. Mounting on the substrate is done during the outer lead bonding (OLB) process and final electrical inspection is conducted after the OLB is completed.

Electrical and external inspections for the flip chip method are conducted after the mounting on the substrate, which is followed by resin application. External inspection for this method is very difficult because the bonding area is concealed by the face-down mounted chip.

The defects most typical in solder bump connections are lack of contact between bumps and the opposite electrode (opens) and shorts, as indicated in Fig. 2. This type of defect is impossible to detect by external inspection. The detection of the defect must to be discovered by functional inspection after mounting on the substrate. Defective chips are replaced before resin application.

Bonding inspection is conducted to test the reliability level at the bonding area. Normally, bonding inspection involves destructive breakage and is conducted only occasionally during mass production after process conditions are determined. Bonding inspections differ depending on the types of mounting methods (Fig. 3). Testing wire bonding involves determining tensile and shear strength at the bonding area. To test tensile strength, a hook is installed at the middle of the wire to evaluate the strength of the wire. The ideal breakage is at the middle but, depending on the position of breakage and mode, the bonding conditions can be evaluated.

Determination of shear strength involves the application of force on the side of the bonding area. Shear resistance and failure modes are evaluated. The most common failure point for wire bonding is between the aluminum electrodes. Depending on the bonding conditions, cracks can occur on the surface of the bonding area or on the chip itself.

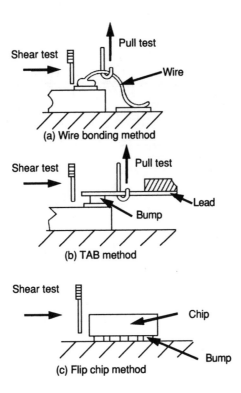

Fig. 3 Bonding inspection methods for each type of mounting.

Bonding inspection for the TAB method is the same as that for the wire bonding method—tensile and bump shearing strength tests. Figures 4 and 5 indicate the breakage modes resulting from the tests. The breakage modes differ depending on bonding conditions, just as in wire bonding.

The only test conducted of bonds mounted using the flip chip method is a shear strength test performed by applying shear force. Due to its structure, the force is applied to the whole chip; the success of bonding can be determined by the breakage mode. For these bonding tests, specialized tensile and shear strength test devices are used. Moreover, scanning electron microscopy (SEM) is used to analyze breaks within the bonding area.

RELIABILITY TESTING TECHNOLOGY

Reliability tests are conducted after the whole chip is covered by resin. Test conditions normally follow MIL standards. The reliability test evaluates whether

Generation mode   Breakage condition

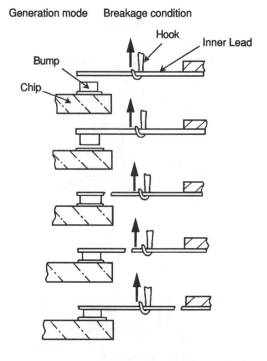

Fig. 4   Breakage modes in the pull test.

changes in chip characteristics have occurred. If such changes have occurred, a determination is made as to whether the defect is in the chip itself or was caused by the mounting process. The defects caused during the mounting process are either due to the bonding conditions or to the performance of protective resin. Evaluating the protective resin involves testing the corrosion process of electrode wire, migration, and stress factor of the resin itself. The quality of protection resin is important because it is supposed to prevent both corrosion due to moisture drawn into the electrode wiring and chip cracks due to stress tolerance of the materials themselves.

When the structure of the mounting is inappropriate, the bonding area is susceptible to distortion and damage. For example, with the TAB method, the stress tolerance decreases because of lead forming at inner and outer leads. When the amount of lead forming is not calculated appropriately, breakage of the lead and distortion of mounted body occur.

Samples that pass reliability tests must be evaluated for minute changes in appearance using not only optical microscopes but high-powered SEM. Figure 6 is a photograph of a minute crack that occurred in the lead area of a TAB-

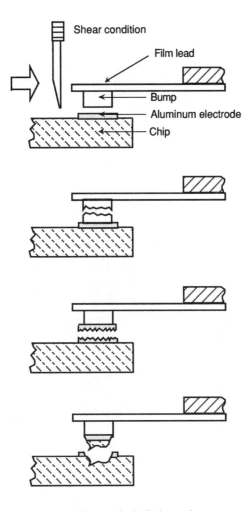

Fig. 5 Breakage modes in the bump shear test.

mounted chip. The cause of this crack is stress added repeatedly to the lead during thermal shock testing. The plated material on the surface is cracked and the copper within is exposed. This observation is possible only with SEM. The minute crack does not show any defect in electrical property at the time; however, exposed copper will corrode in time and eventually causes a lead breakage.

As with reliability testing technology, the reliability testing conditions must be selected depending upon the evaluation categories. The minute defect should be checked closely and detailed information should be provided in order to be used for development of better mounting processes.

TABLE 1   Relation Between Test Items and Evaluation Items

	Evaluation item			
Reliability test items	Bond	Encap-sulation resin	Stress due to thermal expansion and other factors	Lead forming condition
High temperature test	✓			
High temperature high humidity test		✓		
THB test		✓		
Thermal shock test	✓		✓	✓
Temperature shock test	✓		✓	✓
PCT		✓		

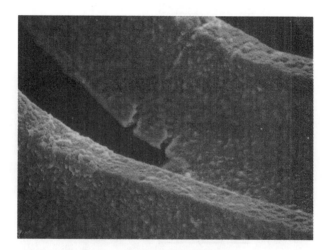

Fig. 6   Microcracks produced in leads.

PROBLEMS AND PROSPECTS

As large scale integration (LSI) chips incorporate more complicated functions and handle a larger volume of information, the size of the chip will inevitably get larger, the electrode pitch will become smaller, and the power per electrode will increase. For evaluating such complicated LSI chips, inspection and reliability technologies must enter a new phase. The electrical and bonding inspections of minute electrodes and smaller pitches will be even more difficult while bonding reliability decreases. In order for COB technologies to be used widely, these problems must be solved.

Repair Technology after COB Interconnect

Kenzo Hatada

Matsushita Electric Industrial Co., Ltd.
Semiconductor Research Center

INTRODUCTION

When defects in mounted electronic parts are detected, the parts must be replaced. Repair is relatively easy when the number of electrodes is small and the electrodes are ruggedly built. Recent large scale integration (LSI) packages have a large number of electrodes and, especially with such technology where the LSI chip is directly mounted on the circuit board (COB), repair has become a difficult issue counterbalancing the advantages provided by LSI technology.

When a mounted chip is removed, the defective chip is subjected to damage; however, the electrode area on the substrate should not be affected so that the new chip can be mounted without further repair. The repair process differs depending on each mounting method. No established repair method exists—each manufacturer has its own method based on accumulated experience. Repair still remains a major element in mounting technology. Even with complete inspection of an LSI chip, process conditions during the mounting can cause defects in chips. The basis for basic ground of repair technology is detection of the defective chip at the earliest possible stage and repair without damage to the substrate.

REPAIR TECHNOLOGY FOR EACH MOUNTING METHOD

This paper outlines differences in repair strategies for each mounting method. The method as well as stages of repair differ depending on the mounting method.

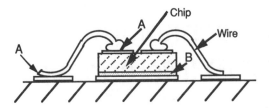

Fig. 1   Repair locations in wire bonding.

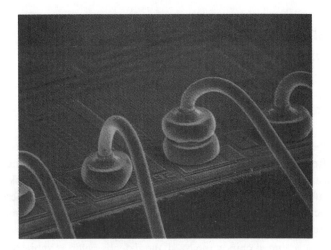

Fig. 2   Wire bond repair examples.

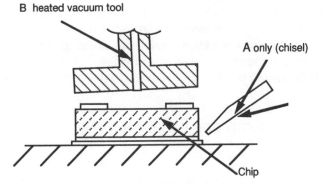

Fig. 3   Wire bonding chip repair method examples.

Repair of chips attached using wire bonding can be divided into two major stages. Figure 1 indicates the repair area when wire bonding is used. *A* indicates a connection defect of the wire, *B* indicates a defective chip. Defects of wire connections can be repaired only on chips mounted using wire bonding. *A* would include wire connection defects of the aluminum electrode on the chip, connection defects of the outer terminal and wire, or the breakage of the wire itself. In case this type of defect occurs, a defective wire can be removed using tweezers with fine points. During this removal process, it is important not to touch other wires and to take as much wire from the connection area as possible. A wire that is connected to aluminum electrodes or outer terminals, however, cannot be removed easily. In this case, a new wire is connected on top of the defective wire (Fig. 2). The repair of this wire is normally conducted using a manually operated device, a costly component of the mounting process.

The repair of the chip itself gets more complicated. There are two methods in repair technology and both methods use a chisel. The first method mechanically peels off the bottom of the chip from the substrate surface (Fig. 3; A). The second method uses heat applied to the chip itself to loosen the bond of the chip to the substrate surface (Fig. 3; B).

When the chip itself is connected with conductive paste, method B of Fig. 3 is more effective. This method is also recommended for solder-bonded chips, except a higher temperature must be applied to the chip. Recent bonding methods using organic bonding agents require both heating and peeling from the side because of the higher bonding strength. It is very rare to have no or little damage to the chip. After the chip is removed, any bond that remains at the die bond area is removed with a tool such as an NT cutter, where a new die bond adhesive agent is applied; a new chip is then die-bonded and wire-bonded. Because heating is necessary during repair processes involving both the wire and the chip, it is best if this complicated process can be avoided. In reality, the use of specialized tools and processes to repair boards is inevitable.

Repair technology for the TAB method is categorized in two types depending on the mounting formation. Figure 4a indicates face-up mounting with the chip itself die-bonded on an integrated circuit (IC) substrate. Figure 4b indicates a face-down mounting with the outer leads connected to the substrate. With the structure in Fig. 4a, the outer lead area is removed from the substrate and the die-bonded chip on the substrate is removed. With the structure in Fig. 4b, the outer lead is removed the same way as in Fig. 4a, then the lead area is heated with the heater that can add heat to outer leads. The alloyed layer is reflowed and the chip area is normally vacuumed.

The repair method shown in Fig. 4a is, however, complicated and difficult. When the outer lead is removed from the electrode on the substrate, only a few leads can be heated and then the leads are picked up by a tweezer one at the time. This is because of the fact that chip itself is die bonded, making removal difficult.

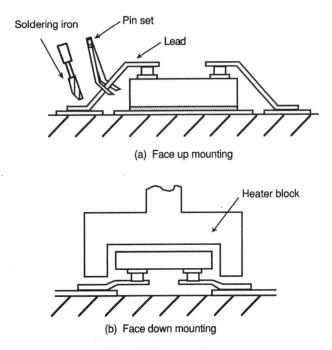

(a) Face up mounting

(b) Face down mounting

Fig. 4   TAB repair examples.

Removing leads one at the time requires experience and any mistake can damage the electrodes on the substrate. When all the leads are removed, the die bonded chip is removed. This method requires heating the chip itself and applying force to the side of the chip, similar to the procedure for wire bonding repair.

The maximum temperature of added heat during the repair differs depending on the types of outer lead bonding (solder, gold-tin eutectic alloy, isotropic conductive sheet, photosetting insulator resin). In order to reconnect the new wire after the chip is removed, any residue on the electrodes must be scraped off and the planarity of the electrode surface must be checked. Metallic residue can be scraped off while adding heat, and organic residues can be removed with appropriate solvents. When leads are bonded with metal adhesive, the remaining metal materials such as solder and gold on the electrodes are insufficient to complete the repair. Thus, new lead bonding of TAB package may, in this case, need an additional supply of solder material or the area where the leads of the defective chip have been bonded are avoided and a new spot is chosen. In the latter case, a TAB package specifically designed for repair is needed, as the bonding position is different. With the TAB method, even when only the lead itself is broken, defective leads cannot be repaired as with wire bonding. Both chip and lead defects require the replacement of the entire TAB package.

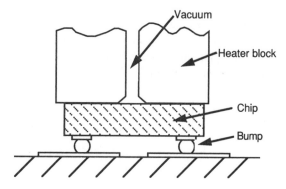

Fig. 5 Flip chip repair examples.

Similarly, repair technology for flip chip–mounted chips cannot be done for connection leads—replacement of the entire chip is necessary. When the solder bump method is used, the chip is heated to the melting point of the solder and the chip is then removed. Heating the chip is performed by applying a heater block against the back of the chip, followed by vacuum suction of the chip (Fig. 5). Because the volume of solder changes after the chip is removed from the substrate, the new chip should be mounted temporarily at low temperatures on the substrate to test electrical properties before reflow is completed. This causes less damage to the electrodes. Reflow of the solder material is done at a set temperature after the repair to achieve a complete bonding. A problem in flip chip repair is the tendency to damage the electrodes because of the small bonding area. It is thus necessary to conduct an electrical inspection on the chip itself and choose the appropriate tools and devices for the repair.

In any repair technology, damage to the substrate or neighboring chips is common. Mounting previously inspected packages is the key to minimizing repair. TAB packages are commonly used for mounting a large number of chips.

PROBLEMS TO BE SOLVED AND FUTURE PROSPECTS

Repair processes are better avoided as much as possible during production. In order to reduce the number of repairs, inspection of LSI chips can be conducted thoroughly, but with chips mounted by wire bonding and flip chip methods, the set frequency and voltage is added at high temperature, and then screened. Because burn-in inspection is not possible, repair technology is required.

In the future, development of devices that allow burn-in inspection at the chip stage will be introduced. Recently, a new development has emerged in which the chip as a whole can be inspected in burn-in condition, using an isotropic conducting sheet (silicone rubber type). When the electrical inspection can be performed on the chip as a whole, repair technology becomes obsolete. The problem of the reduction of connection points needs to be solved first. Mounting methods with fewer connection points are desirable.

Part 6

Multichip Modules
and
Printed Circuit Board
Technologies

Latest Technology Trends in Multichip Modules

Kenzo Hatada

Matsushita Electric Industrial Co., Ltd.
Semiconductor Research Center

INTRODUCTION

With the advancement of electronic equipment, packaging technology became essential in all fields. As a result, various packaging technologies were developed and commercialized. To enhance functions and increase capacity, electronic equipment has developed a new configuration in which many dies are mounted on a substrate so as to form a circuit function. This construction is called the *multichip module*. In addition, trends show that while electronic equipment further gains functions and capacity by using mutichip modules, it becomes more compact.

In the past, electronic equipment was composed mainly of hybrid integrated circuits (ICs) in which C and R chip components and ICs are mounted. But these are being replaced by multichip modules whose primary components are ICs alone because of the advancement of LSIs and the arrival of digital circuits. The applications of hybrid ICs tend to be limited to components such as specific circuit function parts.

Depending on the devices and electronic equipment for which multichip modules are used, the die mounting technologies (i.e., chip interconnect) vary greatly. This is because multichip module technology must meet the different requirements for each device or piece of electronic equipment.

TRENDS IN MULTICHIP PACKAGING TECHNOLOGY

Trends in Multichip Packaging Technology

Multichip packaging technology [1] allows mounting many large scale integration (LSI) devices on a substrate and can be broadly divided into two types (Fig. 1). The first type is a multichip packaging technology whose primary component is the functional substrate. Typical products include LCD modules and thermal printers. In the packaging technology of this field, the construction of pixels and heating elements are more important than the packaging technology for dies, and inexpensive packaging technologies are required rather than high-level packaging technologies. For this reason, fine-pitch, high-pin-count inter-connection technology has been actively developed from early on. Most multi-chip technologies for the functional substrate use a technique in which dies are arranged two-dimensionally. Dies to be mounted have rectangular shapes because of the trend for fine pitch and downsizing.

The second type of multichip module is a packaging technology whose primary components are the LSI device. So-called circuit modules such as memory modules and microprocessor modules for computers are of this type. While this multichip packaging technology aims at large capacity and high functions, high density is also an important technical issue. There are two-dimensional and three-dimensional packaging methods. The two-dimensional method is used for microprocessor modules and the three-dimensional method is used for memory modules.

In modules for microprocessors, dies with different functions, such as gate array and memory, are mounted on a multilayer wiring substrate at a fine pitch with high density, and are completed as a module that functions as a circuit. Important module characteristics are high speed and power dissipation. As high-function computers are becoming more compact, this technology is indispensable as a next-generation packaging technology for the future.

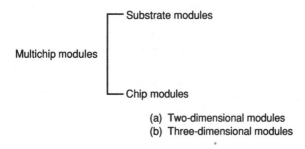

Multichip modules — Substrate modules

— Chip modules

(a) Two-dimensional modules
(b) Three-dimensional modules

Fig. 1 Classification of multichip modules.

In packaging memory modules, the amount of memory capacity that can be stored in a limited thickness and volume determines the product's added value. In a packaging method in which LSIs are arranged in two dimensions, the packaging density cannot be improved. As a result, packaging methods have been developed in which LSIs are mounted on both sides of a substrate or stacked (Fig. 2). In packaging of memory modules, how to deal with noncommon pins for signal processing is the issue. This is especially important when LSIs are arranged three-dimensionally. Among multichip packaging technologies whose primary component is the LSI, memory modules are expected to advance greatly.

Multichip Packaging Technology and the Functional Substrate

Liquid crystal modules are a typical product of multichip packaging technology whose primary component is a functional substrate. Companies have developed various methods for packaging liquid crystal modules but the current mainstream is tape automated bonding (TAB).

TAB was introduced in liquid crystal modules because the pads of liquid crystal panels and the outer leads of a TAB package can be bonded relatively easily by using an anisotropic conductive sheet. Consequently, development of TAB and anisotropic conductive sheets advanced rapidly and the market share of TAB reached 3% of IC packages.

In liquid crystal modules, it is necessary to reduce the packaging area and increase the added value of the product. Thus conventional packaging methods in which TAB packages are arranged two-dimensionally have changed to three-dimensional packaging methods in which TAB packages are folded and stacked. These packaging methods will maximize the special strengths of TAB.

On the other hand, applications for liquid crystal modules are expanding from view finders of TV cameras to computer displays and large-screen TVs. As displays make advances in resolution and color, there is a trend toward narrower

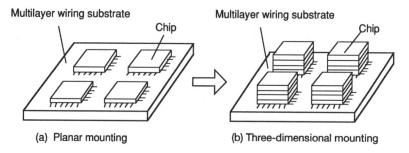

(a) Planar mounting   (b) Three-dimensional mounting

Fig. 2 Chip module mounting methods.

pad pitch and higher pin count. A packaging method is needed to accommodate these trends. TAB packages can already accommodate a pad pitch of 100 μm, but crosstalk is likely to occur in anisotropic conductive sheets. Further, packaging cost must be kept low to hold down the cost of liquid crystal modules.

It is anticipated that chip-on-glass (COG) will solve the issues encountered by TAB in liquid crystal modules, and companies are shifting in this direction. Table 1 contains COG methods that various companies are applying to liquid crystal modules [2]. Many COG technologies using organic materials have been developed in which the LSI is bonded to the glass substrate by using conductive adhesives or resin balls. The objective is to bond the liquid crystal panel's pads to the LSI's pads with as little processing as possible. The Japanese company, Citizen, has had good results over a prolonged time with an interconnect method using organic materials shown in Fig. 3a [3]. In this method, bumps are formed on the LSI, conductive paste is transferred onto the bumps, and the bumps are bonded to indium tin oxide pads of the liquid crystal panel. The bumps are

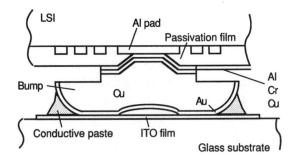

(a) Interconnect method using conductive resin (Citizen)

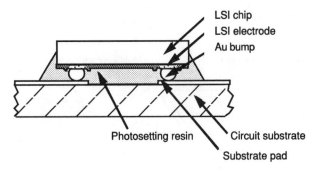

(b) Microbump bonding method (Matsushita)

Fig. 3   Resin materials used in chip on glass technology.

TABLE 1 COG Methods of Various Companies

Company	Bump formation	Pressure, thermal processing	Connection pitch* (µm)	Connection method	Panel processing	Chip processing	Repair method
Citizen	Au (Cu) bump on the chip	80 to 120°C 1.4 g/bump	216 (100)	Ag-Pd paste	None	Bump formation	Chip heating
Matsushita (Microbump bonding)	Au bump on the chip	Normal temp. 10 to 20 g/bump	50 (1)	Resin contraction stress	None	Bump formation	Chip heating
Seiko Epson	Spherical bumps printed on the substrate	150 to 200°C 10 to 25 g/bump	130 (60)	Au-plated resin balls	Resin ball formation Adhesive coating	None	Chip heating
Toshiba	Au-In bump on the chip	Substrate: 55 to 60°C Chip: 120 to 150°C 20 g/bump	130 (50)	In alloy	None	Bump formation	Chip heating
Matsushita (Stud bump bonding)	Ball bump on the chip	100 to 120°C 50 to 70 g/bump	100 to 110	Ag paste	None	Ball bump formation	Chip heating**
Sharp	Au film on the chip	Normal temp. 20 to 30 g/bump	300 (50)	Au-plated resin ball	None	Resin ball formation granular adhesive coating	Chip heating
Oki Electric	Au bump on the chip	170 to 200°C 20 to 50 g/bump	200 (150)	Anisotropic conductive sheet	None	Bump formation	Chip heating***
Casio	(Necessary)	180°C	80 (40)	Resin ball (resin coat on Au plating)	None	(Required)	Chip heating

* Actual pitch achieved; figures in parentheses indicate possible pitch. **Repair is done before hardening. ***Repair is fairly difficult.

formed over the entire surface of the LSI (instead of only the periphery). The bumps are made of copper and are gold plated. Currently, a bonding pitch of 150 μm is possible.

Figure 3b shows the microbump bonding method [4]. The LSI pads and the LCD substrate pads are pressed together and bonded using the contraction stress of photosetting insulating resin to obtain an electrical connection. In this interconnect method, photosetting insulating resin is first applied to the pads on the substrate. These pads and the LSI pads are aligned and pressure is applied simultaneously with UV irradiation. When the substrate is transparent, UV rays are irradiated from the substrate side. When the substrate is opaque, UV rays are irradiated around the LSI to cure the resin surrounding the LSI. The unexposed resin on the LSI surface is cured at ambient temperature. After UV irradiation is complete, the pressure is removed. Electrical connection can be obtained in this way. The special features of this method are: 1) interconnections with fine pitch and super-high pin count can be achieved because pads are simply bonded with pressure and insulating resin is present between pads and 2) because the pads are being pressed together, stress due to thermal expansion can be alleviated in the bond by the sliding action of the pads. Several thousand bonds have already been achieved at a 10-μm pitch in practical applications.

For applications such as LCD modules and thermal printers, which incorporate multichip packaging technology on a functional substrate, interconnect methods are shifting from wire bonding and TAB methods to chip on board (COB). Furthermore, COB is evolving from intermetallic bonding to new bonding methods using resin materials.

Multichip Packaging of LSIs

Multichip packaging of LSIs can be divided into the packaging of LSIs having identical functions and of LSIs having different functions. Most of these methods are used for computer-related products.

In packaging LSIs having the same function, the dies can be arranged either in a plane or three-dimensionally. Figure 4 shows a circuit block for mid-size and large computers where dies having the same function are mounted on a multilayer substrate. Interconnection of the die and the substrate's pads can be done with wire bonding, TAB, or flip chip methods.

The latest development in interconnect technology is three-dimensional packaging, used especially in the configuration of memory modules. In memory modules, higher density is required because many memory chips need to be mounted within a limited thickness or volume. Figure 5 shows a configuration in which LSIs are mounted on end. TAB leads are used for the interconnection. While many dies can fit within a particular distance, the entire package is thicker because of the TAB packaging.

Fig. 4   Multichip module with TAB packages.

Fig. 5   A memory module with vertically mounted TAB packages.

Figure 6 shows a configuration in which dies are stacked on top of each other [5]. The memory chips are packaged in TAB and stacked at the die level by varying the length of the outer leads and the amount of lead-forming for every level of the stack. As this indicates, an issue in die stacking is how to handle the noncommon pins. In the memory module in Fig. 6, each inner lead connected to a noncommon die pin is branched out into four outer leads. Three of these outer leads are severed so that a different lead remains for each level of the stack. In this way, the four dies packaged in the same TAB tape can be connected to the substrate with their noncommon pins separated. A 1-megabyte memory module has been made from eight stacks of four 256K static RAMs.

In memory modules, where the key concern is to create high-density modules by using thin packages, development of three-dimensional packaging meth-

Fig. 6 A memory module with four dies stacked in TAB packages.

ods is being anticipated as the most optimal approach. Three-dimensional packaging is also an important technology in future multichip packaging technology.

On the other hand, multichip packaging for dies having different functions is a technology for the future. It involves the mounting of different dies such as gate arrays, memories, and microprocessors onto the same substrate to form a function circuit. As computers are enhanced in functionality and reduced in size, high density multichip modules become indispensable. To downsize the modules, the wiring density of the module substrate will approach a 1-μm design rule, which is in the range of a semiconductor process. The pad dimensions will become finer, progressing from the conventional 100 μm square to approximately 10 μm square. Thus, the package construction will be able to achieve both high density and high speed. Currently, development is at the stage of selecting the substrate to be used and the fine-pitch, high-pin-count interconnect method.

FUTURE ISSUES AND PROSPECTS

With the advancement of LSIs and electronic equipment, multichip packaging technology will be an increasingly important technology. In the multichip packaging technology whose primary component is the functional substrate, the trend shows that the technology is shifting to COB, which is suitable for low cost and high density. In COB, the inspection of the die itself and the repair will be important but, presently, there is no established method. New technology development is hoped for in the future.

In the multichip packaging of LSIs, because high functionality, large capacity and high speed are required, an interconnect pitch of several microns to several tens of microns will be required. This calls for a technology that can provide interconnection for several thousand pins and three-dimensional packaging. At present, the trend has already become apparent. Multichip packaging technology will be needed for new LSIs and new electronic equipment, and will play an important role in adding value to new products.

REFERENCES

[1] "Trends in packaging technology," *Nihon Keizai Shinbun,* January 21, 1991.

[2] K. Hatada, "Driver attachment by bare chip COG," *Semiconductor World Special Issue,* p. 253, September 1, 1990.

[3] Iinuma, "The present status and issues of modules by resin interconnect," *11th Electronics Packaging Technology Workshop Sponsored by SHM,* January 30, 1991.

[4] K. Hatada et al., "LED array modules by new technology microbump bonding method," *IEEE Trans CHMT,* vol. 13, no.3, September 1990.

[5] K. Hatada et al., "T-BTAB application for vertically integrated interconnect," *Proc ISHM '90.*

Multichip Module Packaging Technology in Computers

Toshihiko Watari

NEC Corp.

INTRODUCTION

The concept of multichip modules evolved mainly from the demand for high-density packaging for computers. In computers that consist of complex circuits, it is always an issue to enhance performance and shrink size. At the same time, shrinking size (i.e., high-density packaging) is essential to enhance performance. This paper discusses the changes in multichip modules as a means of high-density packaging for computers, and an example of the latest technology.

CONSTRUCTION OF MULTICHIP PACKAGES

Broadly speaking, two types of construction can be considered for multichip packages as shown in Fig. 1 [1].While the wiring substrate basically has only the top surface and the underside, a minimum of four packaging elements must be arranged on the wiring substrate. These are input/output devices (I/Os), patterns for interconnect, large scale integration (LSI) devices, and cooling paths. These four package elements must be arranged on two sides—the top surface and the underside.

Figure 1a is an example in which the pattern layer, I/Os, and LSIs are arranged on the top surface of the wiring substrate and the underside is used for cooling. Materials with good thermal conductivity must be used for the wiring substrate in this case because the substrate itself becomes a heat path. Generally, an alumina ceramic substrate is used. Because the pattern layer also is a heat dis-

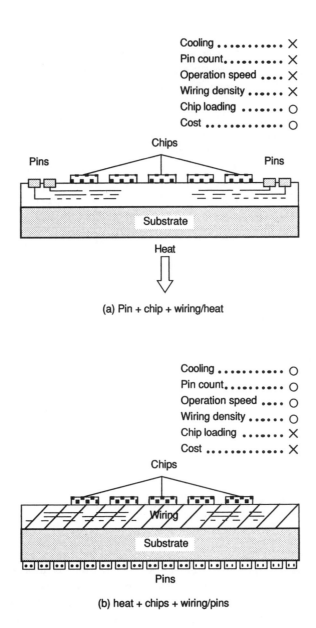

Fig. 1 Multichip package mounting. The O and X in the figure refer to various advantages and disadvantages occurring in case (a) and case (b).

sipation path, low thermal resistance is required of the insulating layer. Thus, a thick-film insulating layer consisting of a mixture of alumina and glass powder is used. Thick-film or thin-film gold patterns are used for the pattern conductors. I/Os are joined with the connectors on the motherboard by arranging pads on the edges of the substrate. While LSIs are arranged on the patterns and bonded to the die pads that are formed on the patterns, leads are bonded to pads by tape automated bonding (TAB) and these leads are also formed on the patterns.

Figure 1b is an example in which the pattern layer, LSIs, and the cooling side are arranged on the top surface of the wiring substrate and I/Os are arranged on the underside. There are no restrictions for the thermal conductivity of the pattern layer and the substrate's materials in this case because the surface of the substrate is the cooling path and the heat does not go through the pattern layer and the substrate. The heat that is generated by LSIs can be dissipated very efficiently because a cooling device can be attached directly onto the LSIs. On the other hand, I/Os can be formed on the whole underside in grids. Therefore, quite a few I/Os can be formed. But LSIs need to be connected to the pattern layer in the so-called face-down format. For this reason, restrictions occur in the interconnect method of LSIs. Wire-bonding cannot be used.

As described above, the packaging formats shown in Fig. 1 have both advantages and disadvantages. The advantages and disadvantages are shown in Fig. 1 with o (good) and x (poor). In short, the packaging format in Fig. 1b excels in cooling ability and I/O count. Also, organic materials can be used whose thermal resistance is large but dielectric constant is small. As a result, the pattern delay time can be reduced. At the same time, because the surface is smooth and fine, fine patterns can be formed, which in turn presents an advantage. That way, higher-density patterns can be realized when the number of layers is the same. On the other hand, the packaging format in Fig. 1a offers a special feature in which various methods can be used for packaging dies because dies are attached face up, and this format has the advantage of low cost.

CHANGES IN MULTICHIP PACKAGING FOR HIGH-PERFORMANCE COMPUTERS

Table 1 contains multichip packages that are used for NEC's large computers. The changes in the technology will be described by using them as examples [2], [3], [4]. The packaging format in these cases is the same as that of Fig. 1a. With the advancement of LSI technology, the packaging density was improved and the progress of the multichip packaging technology is visible. In these examples, TAB has been used consistently for the attachment of LSIs since 1975. Figure 2 shows the the multichip package that was used for ACOS S1500 as a typical example of the packaging format shown in Table 1. The multichip packaging

TABLE 1 Mainframe Computer Multichip Packaging Technology

Generation (year)	First generation (1977)	Second generation (1981)	Generation 2.5 (1983)	Third generation (1985)
Substrate dimension (mm)	80 × 80	80 × 80	80 × 80	100 × 100
TAB chip number (units)	Maximum 110	60	Maximum 56	36
Integration degree/TAB chip (gate)	Maximum 200	200	300/2,000	1,000
TAB pin count (pins)	24/40	40	52/132	176
TAB lead pitch (µm)	400	300	280	160
TAB connection	Au/Au	Au/Au	Au/Au	Au/Au
LSI package pin count	240	296	420	2,177
LSI package power consumption	Maximum 45	Maximum 55	Maximum 90	Maximum 250
LSI package maximum gate number	3,500	6,000	10,000	32,000
Wiring substrate material	Alumina ceramic	Alumina ceramic	Alumina ceramic	Alumina ceramic
Wiring	Thick film	Thin film	Thin film	Thin film
Insulation material	Alumina glass thick film	Alumina glass thick film	Alumina glass thick film	Polyimide
Wiring width (µm)	120	50	50	25
Wiring pitch (µm)	240	200	160	75
Signal wiring layer number	2	2	2	2

Fig. 2   Example of a multichip package.

Fig. 3   Composite multilayer ceramic substrate package.

technologies shown in Table 1 are the ones that were used for mainframe computers from 1975 though 1985.

The first attempt for the packaging in Fig. 1b was the CMCS (composite multilayer ceramic substrate) package shown in Fig. 3 [5]. In Fig. 3, the TABed bare dies are attached face down. The wiring substrate is made by forming multilayer patterns of thin-film patterns and alumina/glass thick-film insulation on the surface of the glass ceramic base in which the power and ground layers are formed. The special feature of this multichip packaging is that a TABed bare die can be attached. In other words, the leads of the TAB package are bonded directly on the patterns by thermocompression bonding. With this technique, die packaging density can be improved. In the example in Fig. 3, 49 TABed dies are attached onto a 10×10 cm substrate. But because an organic material made of alumina and glass is used for the insulating layers, the dielectric constant is unable to be lowered and the pattern propagation speed has not been substantially improved compared with the conventional alumina ceramic substrate.

PACKAGING TECHNOLOGY OF SUPERCOMPUTER "SX-3"

Packaging Hierarchy

In supercomputers, the system's performance enhancement is the highest priority issue, and with the use of high-performance LSI technology, multichip packaging also became essential from the standpoint of increased speed of interconnects. In addition, to meet the demand for high-speed interconnects, cooling, high-density patterns, and high pin-counts, the use of packaging as in Fig. 1b became essential. Figure 4 shows the packaging hierarchy of NEC's SX-3 supercomputer [6].

The special features of packaging shown in Fig. 4 are the TABed die, the super-small chip carrier FTC (flipped TAB carrier) that stores the TABed die, and the 22.5×22.5 cm polyimide ceramic substrate on which 100 FTCs are attached. First, by using FTC, high-efficient cooling became possible for LSIs whose power consumption reached 33 W because of high integration. In addition, high-density packaging was made possible in high-pin-count interconnects of LSIs. Also, the polyimide ceramic substrate is capable of interconnecting as many as 100 high-pin-count FTCs and approximately 12,000 pins on the underside of the substrate with little delay at high density, which greatly contributes to making the entire packaging compact. The details of this packaging technology are discussed below.

LSI Packaging (FTC)

Generally, the I/O count required for gate array LSIs increases gradually on the basis of Rent's rule as the integration improves. Therefore, the ability to achieve high-pin-count interconnects at high density becomes the goal. Various methods can be considered for taking out a large number of pins from LSIs (discussed later) but we adopted face-down TAB because of the ease of cooling. Figure 5 shows a cross-section of the FTC. In the FTC, the TABed die is attached onto the substrate face down. I/Os are provided on the underside of the substrate and the heat path is through the surface. In addition, because I/Os are formed in grids on the underside of the substrate, a large number of I/Os can exist in a small space.

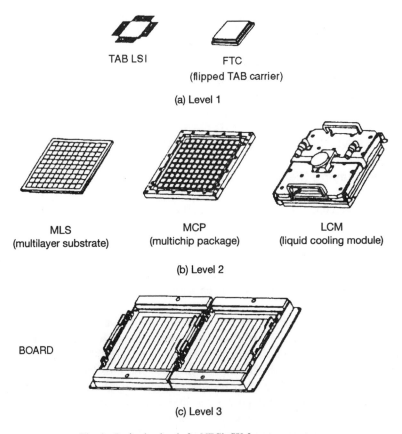

Fig. 4   Packaging levels for NEC's SX-3 supercomputer.

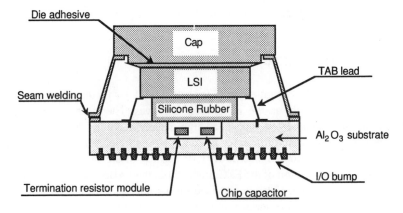

Fig. 5   Cross-section of flipped TAB carrier.

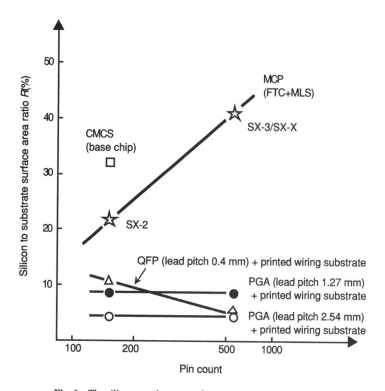

Fig. 6 The silicon to substrate surface area ratio for various packages.

When the packaging densities of LSIs are compared, the ratio of the area of silicon (i.e., die) to the area of the substrate on which it is attached can be used. Figure 6 is the comparison of the ratio of the area of silicon to the area of the substrate among various LSI packages [6]. As Fig. 6 clearly indicates, the FTC does not decrease in packaging density with high-pin-count LSIs. While the packaging density of course depends on what wiring substrate is combined, the FTC maximizes its features in combination with a polyimide ceramic substrate. As Fig. 5 clearly shows, the silicon itself is directly die-bonded to the cap of the FTC, thus a cap material should be used whose coefficient of thermal expansion is similar to that of silicon and whose thermal conductivity is good. For example, very high heat dissipation can be obtained by using a copper–tungsten alloy or aluminum nitride.

Wiring Substrate (Polyimide Ceramic Substrate)

According to Rent's rule, the I/Os between LSIs and I/Os for the substrate's external connections increase as the number of logic gates on the substrate

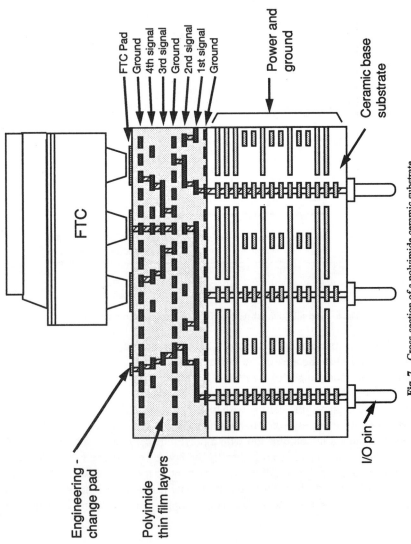

FTC Pad
Ground
4th signal
3rd signal
Ground
2nd signal
1st signal
Ground

Power and ground

FTC

Engineering - change pad

Polyimide thin film layers

Ceramic base substrate

I/O pin

Fig. 7 Cross-section of a polyimide ceramic substrate.

increases. The ability to accommodate such a large number of patterns is required of the wiring substrate and it is desirable to minimize the signal propagation delay due to the connections. The polyimide ceramic substrate is optimum for such applications. As the cross-section in Fig. 7 shows, the alumina ceramic substrate is used for the base substrate and power and ground patterns are formed within it. By providing through-holes that go through the surface to the underside of the substrate, the pattern layer on the surface is connected to I/O pins for external connections. On the surface of the substrate thin film, multilayer patterns are formed whose insulating layers are made of polyimide resin. Because polyimide pattern layers have a small dielectric constant of 3.5 compared with a dielectric constant of 9 for the alumina ceramic multilayer wiring board, the signal delay can be reduced by approximately 40%. Further, because the insulating layers are resin, there is a special feature that the surface is very smooth and fine patterns are easily formed. Compared with general printed wiring boards, the substrate's coefficient of thermal expansion is small. This makes it easier to use not only alumina but silicon for packaging. In addition, a very large number of pins can be provided on the substrate. As discussed above, the polyimide ceramic wiring substrate is optimum for the interconnect of high-density, high-speed logic circuits.

Multichip Package

Figure 8 shows the appearance of the multichip package for the SX-3. Attached onto a 22.5 × 22.5 cm substrate are 100 FTCs. Because the maximum gate count per LSI is 20,000 gates, a single package has a maximum of 2,000,000

Fig. 8 Multichip package for the SX-3.

gates. A processor can be constructed on a multichip package perfectly. A frame called a *flange* is attached to the substrate in order to attach I/O pins on the underside of the board that reach approximately 12,000 pins at once with zero insertion force.

Cooling Module

With the improvement in the packaging density, the power consumption on the multichip package increased. In the case of the SX-3, the maximum reaches 3.8 kW. When it is converted to wattage per unit area, it is 7.9 W/cm^2. To maintain the junction temperature of the LSIs at 55°C or below on average, the thermal resistance per LSI must be designed at 0.6°C/W. Such a low thermal resistance is impossible to achieve with air-cooling. Therefore, liquid cooling is the only method that can be used. Figure 9 shows the appearance of the cooling module.

CONCLUSION

Discussed above are the changes and practical applications of the multichip module as a package for computers. We have great expectations for the advancement of packaging technologies focusing on multichip modules in the future. As TAB is applied to volume products, it is hoped that these technologies will be disseminated widely to more common products.

Fig. 9   Cooling module for the SX-3.

REFERENCES

[1] T. Watari, "High density packaging technology for supercomputer," *IMC 1990 Proc,* Tokyo, May 30–June 1, 1990.

[2] K. Ishii et al., "High-integration packaging technology of mainframe computers and its role," *Nikkei Electronics,* pp. 100–119, April 18, 1977.

[3] M. Akino et al., "Technology for ACOS System 1000," *NEC Technical Report,* vol. 35, no. 5, pp. 38–43, May 1982.

[4] K. Izumiya et al., "Hardware for ACOS System 1500 Series," *NEC Technical Report,* vol. 38, no. 11, pp. 9–21, October 30, 1985.

[5] A. Dohya et al., "A composite multilayer ceramic substrate for high-performance multi-chip packages," *Proc 1987 IEEE Internat. Electronic Manufacturing Technol.,* pp. 102–107, October 1987.

[6] A. Dohya et al., "Packaging technology for the NEC SX-3/SX-X supercomputer," *IEEE ECTC Conf.,* pp. 523–533, May 1990.

[7] B.S. Landman and L. Rosso, "On a pin versus block relationship for partitions of logic graphs," *IEEE Trans. Comput.,* vol. C-20, no. 12, pp. 1469–1479, December 1971.

[8] T. Watari and H. Murano, "Packaging technology for the NEC SX Supercomputer," *IEEE Trans. CHMT,* vol. CHMT-8, no. 4, pp. 462–467, December 1985.

Very Thin Multilayer Substrate Technology

Kenji Sasaoka

Toshiba Electric Industrial Co., Ltd.
Printed Substrate Technology Division

INTRODUCTION

In recent years, electronic equipment has moved further toward personalization, where portability is an important guideline for determining a product's value. This is rapidly promoting advances in making electronic equipment lighter, smaller, and more functional. Toward this end, there is a strong demand for printed wiring boards (PWB) that are thinner, lighter, have a greater number of layers, and denser circuit patterns.

For example, some personal electronic equipment, such as portable computers, electronic pocket notebooks, and mobile phones, have PWBs of four to six layers. In addition, demand for thin, multilayer substrates accompanies increases in the memory capacity of memory cards widely used as external storage devices [3].

In video camcorders, because a large number of components must fit into a limited space, nearly all consumer electronics makers have adopted four-layer, fine pattern substrates and targeted them as an important technology, demanding thinner substrates that are even a few extra grams lighter [2]. In order to meet these demands, board makers are applying various methods to promote technological developments.

At Toshiba, we addressed these demands by marketing a 0.38-mm-thick, four-layer, fine pattern substrate using FR-4 and FR-5 (NEMA grade) glass epoxy as the substrate's base material.

However, the current through-hole plating method that is typical in multilayer substrate technology becomes progressively more complex as the number of layers in the substrate increases. Especially in the case of IVH (interstitial via hole) structured multilayer substrates, fabrication becomes an endlessly complex process. Because of this, it is becoming more and more desirable to simplify the multilayering process. At Toshiba, we use a completely different method from that used to fabricate substrates to date. We are developing plastic multilayer substrate technology to simplify fabrication of multilayer substrates [4], [5].

We have now put this plastic multilayer substrate technology to practical use. The technology we have developed fulfills both the need for ever-thinner multilayer substrates in product specifications as well as the need for simplification in multilayering process [1].

PROCESS PRINCIPLES

Buildup Phenomenon

As shown in Fig. 1, conductive paste is printed on thermoplastic resin film that has had holes drilled in it. This conductive paste is printed on the lower thermoplastic resin film layer as well. By aligning the upper and lower films to the center layer and pressing them together with a heat press, the conductive paste builds up at the holes, effectively connecting the two layers of conductive paste. Consequently, it is not necessary to carry out any special through-hole process to establish conduction. Figure 2 shows a cross-sectional photograph of the through-hole area.

Self-Adhesion Phenomenon

As the temperature rises between the thermoplastic resin film layers, the molecular chains on the surface of the films intertwine. This phenomenon is called *self-adhesion*. At this time, heat press conditions must be strictly maintained to achieve both a macro stabilization to prevent deformation of the wiring patterns formed by the conductive paste, and an opposite micro fluidity for the buildup phenomenon to occur. Using these two phenomena, we have successfully formed multilayer wiring.

SPECIFICATIONS AND MATERIALS OF THE
DEVELOPED PRODUCT

Toshiba has developed very thin, four-layer and eight-layer multilayer substrates. The specifications and materials of these substrates are listed in Table 1.

Presently, our glass epoxy substrates—0.38-mm-thick PWB for four-layer and 1.0-mm-thick PWB for eight-layer—are well known as thin, multilayer sub-

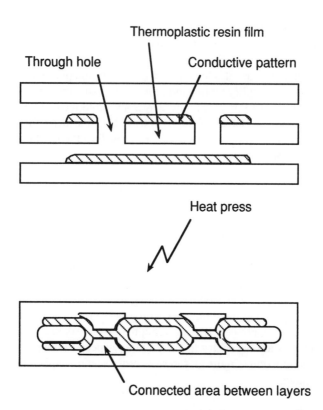

Fig. 1 Example of a multichip package.

TABLE 1 Product Specifications and Materials

Number of layers	4	8
Size (mm)	48 × 75	150 × 250
Thickness (mm)	0.09	0.20
Hole diameter (mm)	0.2	0.3
Land diameter (mm)	0.5	0.75
Minimum pattern width (mm)	0.15	0.15
Minimum pattern pitch (mm)	0.30	0.30
Base material	25 μm thick polyether sulfone	
Conductive material	thermoplastic resin–based Ag paste	

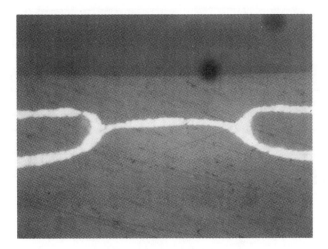

Fig. 2   Cross-sectional photograph of through-hole area.

strates. In comparison, the multilayer substrates now developed are 0.09-mm and 0.20-mm thick for four-layer and eight-layer substrates, respectively.

Both four-layer and eight-layer substrates are made of the same materials. The distinctive characteristics of the substrate materials lie in the use of polyether sulfone film, a thermoplastic resin, as the base material and the use of silver paste as a conductive material to bind the thermoplastic resin.

STRUCTURE OF THE NEW SUBSTRATES

We developed a four-layer and eight-layer substrate. Figure 3 shows a typical cross-section of the four-layer substrate.

The four-layer substrate uses three layers of film. Wiring patterns are printed on both sides of the center film. Two layers of film, each with a printed wiring pattern on the outer surface only, are aligned to cover either side of the center film. The eight-layer substrate has two layers of one-sided film laminated to both sides of the four-layer substrate. This adds up to seven layers of film for the eight-layer substrate.

FABRICATION PROCESS

The fabrication process for these new substrates is depicted in Fig. 4. First, holes are formed in the film. Although the film used here is very thin (25 μm), the holes were made with a drill in the same manner as for a normal PWB.

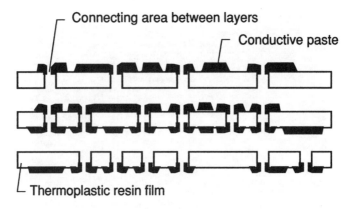

Fig. 3   Cross-section diagram of a 4-layer substrate.

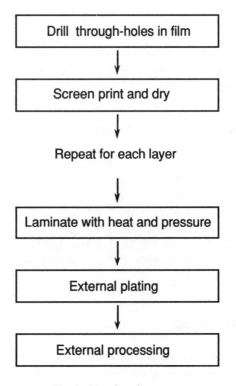

Fig. 4   Manufacturing process.

Next, the circuit pattern is screen printed and baked dry. Silver-based conductive paste is used as the binder of the thermoplastic resin. The pattern pitch is 300 μm for both the four-layer and the eight-layer substrates.

These two processes are repeated for the number of layers in the substrate. For four-layer substrates, holes are drilled three times and printing and baking is carried out four times. For eight-layer substrates, holes are drilled seven times, and printing and baking is carried out eight times. In this way each layer has its own wiring pattern formed.

Next, each layer is stacked and aligned to form a specific construction and then pressed together with a heat press. Process control of this step is the key point of this development. This will be explained below.

The three processes described above finish the structure of the multilayer substrate but, taking into consideration the placing of surface mount parts, copper plating is carried out on the outermost pattern layers when required. Finally, external processing is performed and the very thin, multilayer substrate is completed.

HEAT PRESS

In this development, a parallel plane plate heat press was used. As noted before, in order to obtain the buildup and autohesion phenomena, a specific temperature and range of pressure must be maintained [5].

The relation between temperature and pressure in the development of very thin multilayer substrates is shown in Figure 5. It has been proven that the buildup

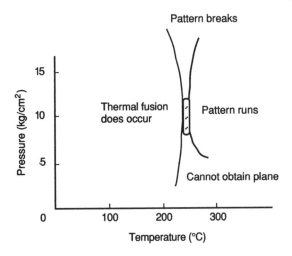

Fig. 5 Relationship between temperature and pressure.

phenomenon at the through-holes and the autohesion phenomenon between the film layers simultaneously occur only in a very narrow range of 235 to 245° C in temperature and 8 to 12 kg/cm^2 in pressure.

Furthermore, tight control of the temperature and pressure profile is critical (see Fig. 6). The point here is that the pressure must be applied after the temperature has become stable, and that the pressure is removed only after the temperature has fallen sufficiently.

TRIAL PRODUCT RESULTS

Four-Layer Substrate

The four-layer substrate developed by Toshiba is shown in Fig. 7. The picture was taken prior to external processing and shows two surfaces. The white area visible in the center of the photograph is the silver-paste printed circuit area.

Table 2 compares the thickness and weight of this substrate against those of a glass epoxy substrate. A 0.4-mm-thick glass epoxy substrate of FR-4 base material was fabricated to the same specifications as the new substrate to compare actual measured values. The four-layer subject substrate was found to be 78% thinner and 72% lighter than the glass epoxy substrate.

Eight-Layer Substrate

The eight-layer substrate is shown in Fig. 8. Like the four-layer substrate, the white area visible in the center is the silver-paste printed circuit area. The densest portion of the pattern has circuit widths of 0.15 mm, with circuit pitches of 0.3 mm.

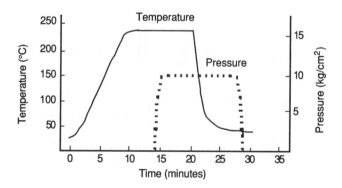

Fig. 6   Temperature and pressure profiles.

Fig. 7 Photograph of four-layer substrate.

TABLE 2 Four-layer Substrate Thickness and Weight Compared with FR-4 Glass Epoxy Substrate

	Thickness (mm)	Weight (g)
FR-4	0.41	2.41
New substrate	0.09	0.67
Reduction in thickness	78%	—
Weight reduction	—	72%
Reduction = (FR-4 − new substrate)/FR-4		

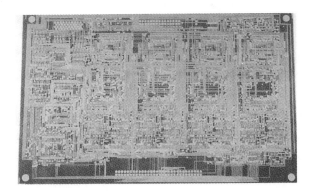

Fig. 8 Photograph of eight-layer substrate.

Table 3 compares the thicknesses and weights of this substrate with a glass epoxy substrate. The glass epoxy substrate is made from FR-4 base material and is an eight-layer substrate with a standard thickness of 1.6 mm. It was fabricated to the same specifications as the new substrate to compare actual measured values. The new eight-layer subject substrate was found to be 88% thinner and 90% lighter than the glass epoxy substrate.

ELECTRICAL CHARACTERISTICS

Table 4 describes representative electrical characteristics of the very thin, multilayer substrate. As a frame of reference, the characteristics of an FR-4 glass epoxy substrate under normal conditions are also given.

We noticed a slight degradation of the new substrate's electrical characteristics due to moisture absorption, but for use as a PWB, sufficient functionality is retained. Also, compared with the characteristics of the glass epoxy substrate, the new substrate, prior to the moisture absorption process, displayed superior characteristics for all items except conductive resistance, which is due to the difference in conductive materials used.

CONCLUSION

As described above, we have developed a product that conforms to the two major trends in PWB: simplification of the fabrication process in multilayer technology and thinner multilayer substrates that will meet product specifications.

The heat resistance level of the very thin, multilayer substrate introduced here is suited to surface mount components that are connected to the substrate by fusible solder or solderless methods. However, in order to have this new PWB accepted widely, it must support the use of eutectic solder, which is currently the most common method used in mounting components. Development of a multi-

TABLE 3 Eight-layer Substrate Thickness and Weight Compared with Glass Epoxy Substrate

	Thickness (mm)	Weight (g)
FR-4	1.66	115.8
New substrate	0.20	10.9
Reduction in thickness	88%	—
Weight reduction	—	90%
Reduction = (FR-4 − new substrate)/FR-4		

TABLE 4   Representative Electrical Characteristics

Test item	Unit	Test conditions	New substrate	FR-4
Conductive sheet resistance	mΩ/sq	C-96/20/65	7.2	0.3
		+ C-96/40/90	7.3	—
Volumetric resistivity	Ω • cm	C-96/20/65	5.6×10^{16}	7.8×10^{15}
		+ C-96/40/90	2.3×10^{16}	—
Surface resistance	Ω	C-96/20/65	6.7×10^{13}	3.6×10^{12}
		+ C-96/40/90	1.4×10^{31}	—
Dielectric constant (1 MHz)		C-96/20/65	3.44	4.54
		+ C-96/40/90	3.60	—
Dielectric loss tangent (1 MHz)		C-96/20/65	0.004	0.017
		+ C-96/40/90	0.010	—
Voltage resistance		DC 2 kV, 1 minute	OK	OK

layer substrate for eutectic solder using the method described above and a highly heat resistant material will be announced soon.

While the new multilayer substrate will be used to replace existing multi-layer substrates, its application does not simply stop there. We intend to continue developing new uses to make the most of this substrate's characteristics, incorporating our customer's needs along the way.

REFERENCES

[1] Sasaoka, Yoshida, Mori, Ohdaira, "Development of very thin, multilayer substrates," *Printed Circuits Associates Fifth Symposium,* pp. 87–88.

[2] Tsuruhara, "Multilayer printed circuit boards hastening smaller and lighter integrated VTR cameras," *Nikkei New Material,* pp. 70–76, August 20, 1990.

[3] Yamamoto, "Technological trends in IC memory cards for external storage devices," *Electronic Surface Mount Technology,* pp. 55–62, July 1990.

[4] Ohdaira, Yoshida, Saito, Ouchi, "Development of a simple process for multilayer printed circuit boards," *Printed Circuits Associates First Symposium Proceeding,* pp. 79–82.

[5] H. Ohdaira, K. Yoshida, K. Sasaoka, "New polymeric multilayer substrates and packaging," *Printed Circuit World Convention,* June 1990, A2/3.

Inspection Technology for Printed Circuit Boards

Shinichi Uno

Toshiba Electrical Industrial Co., Ltd.
Production Technology Research Laboratory

INTRODUCTION

Remarkable progress has been made recently in high density interconnect technology, contributing greatly toward making electronic equipment smaller, lighter, and more functional. Surface mount components are becoming increasingly smaller and printed wiring board patterns increasingly finer.

Printed circuit board (PCB) inspection can be divided into two categories: visual and electrical. These inspections are generally used together. Visual inspection checks items such as the polarity of capacitors and component alignment—items that cannot be detected electrically. The demand for automated visual inspection equipment has grown rapidly [1]. This is caused by the growing dependence on visual inspection as problems arise in making electrical contact with higher density designs, and by the fact that automation is indispensable in light of future manpower shortages and overseas production. In addition to visual inspection, tests are becoming necessary for internal defects such as solder cracks and voids, as well as for the inner condition of compound components.

Many diverse methods and techniques have been developed for inspecting printed circuit boards. This paper discusses recent development trends in inspection technology, focusing on inspecting the condition of mounted parts and soldering.

INSPECTION TECHNOLOGY FOR MOUNTED PARTS

Inspecting the condition of parts mounted on the PCB is a process that requires a large number of inspectors on the production floor. Following this inspection is the soldering process. When defects are overlooked here, laborious rework is required. Testing in the past has concentrated on naked eye tests but as PCBs have become more dense, new test methods and equipment have been developed over the past few years.

Functions Required of Automated Inspection

Table 1 lists the functions needed in an automated inspection system. Inspection reliability involves two elements: false accepts (i.e., a defective part judged to be good) and false rejects (i.e., a good part judged to be defective). Of course, false accepts must be eliminated, but the practicality of the system on a production line is determined by the degree in which false rejects are decreased.

Using the placing machine as a measure, a desirable inspection speed should be approximately four to five times faster. If the placing speed is 200 ms per component, the inspection speed must be 40 to 50 ms, requiring extremely high-speed processing.

As PCBs become more diverse, there will be a strong demand to simplify the enormous amount of inspection-related data, such as inspection standards and component descriptions necessary for switching production, as well as a quick way of registering this data.

Technological Issues

Technological issues involve developing 1) detection methods, 2) high-speed processing, and 3) recognition and comparison algorithms.

TABLE 1 Function Requirements for Printed Circuit Board Inspection

Items to be inspected	Rectangular chips, round chips, irregular-shaped chips, minimold transistors, SOP, QFP
Points of inspection	Missing components, positional displacement, skew, direction, tombstones
Reliability	Recognition rate of 99.98% or greater
Speed	At least 50 ms per component

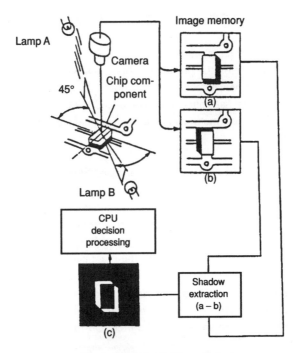

Fig. 1   Principle of oblique shadowing.

Detection Methods. Inspection is complicated by the large number of component types and the complexity of the PCB. Not only are there thousands of types of components, but each type comes in different shapes and colors. Also, circuit patterns and printed type are laid over the weave pattern on the PCB, requiring the development of inspection methods to deal with those factors.

High-speed Processing. The ability to inspect a component in 40 to 50 ms will be vital. To accomplish this, innovations are needed in data compression, dedicated firmware, and multitask processing.

Recognition Algorithm. The nature of the inspection demands an extremely high rate of recognition. For example, if a PCB has 100 components, a recognition rate as high as 99.9% would cause false recognitions to reach several percent. What is needed is a suitable inspection method supported by a precise recognition algorithm.

Technological Trends

Various inspection methods have been developed. These can be divided largely into those that use illumination and optics, those that are based upon vision processing and recognition, and those that employ multiple cameras or color image processing. Inspection devices representative of these methods are discussed below.

Oblique Shadowing. The principles of oblique shadowing are shown in Fig. 1 [2]. This method uses the shadow image of the component, enabling an inspection unaffected by the circuit pattern or printed characters on the surface of the component. Moreover, the image data can be greatly compressed, making high-speed processing possible.

This method involves locating a CCD camera directly over the sample with lights shining obliquely from either side. By illuminating the component from one side and then from the other, two images can be captured (Figs. 1a and 1b). A shadow can be detected on the edges of the component for each of the two images. Taking the absolute value of the difference in the concentration of the two images, an image with a shadow adjoining only the chip component can be extracted, as shown in Fig. 1c. From this image, conditions such as positional displacement, skew, or missing parts can be found.

Sectional Lighting. There are many inspection methods using sectional lighting. This method concentrates on the shape of the sample and does not require shading contrast in the inspection area for detection. Another advantage is that this method has a smaller amount of data to be processed.

Figures 2 and 3 show examples of PCBs inspected by sectional lighting. Figure 2 is an example of sectional lighting using multiple slits of light [3]. Here, 63 slits of light are emitted for each of the X and Y directions, allowing the inspection time for one part to be decreased (40 ms/part) when compared with that using a single slit of light.

Figure 3 is an example of two slits of light shining simultaneously at right angles to each other [4]. An optical scanner is placed in the light path so that the slit position of the light can be controlled. This enables precise inspection that is sensitive to the mounting position as well as to individual inspection items. Also, the sample can be inspected very accurately by changing the intensity of the light emitted from the slit to suit the particular sample.

Color Image Recognition. One method that has been announced distinguishes the part image from the PCB image by means of image recognition based on the differences in color between the part and the PCB [5]. This method divides the image of the PCB into seven color regions and processes each region with eight color parameters, such as brightness and hue. This test is carried out on the placement position with respect to the lands, employing an inspection algorithm that resembles actual visual inspection. Figure 4 shows the configuration of the system and the color separation of the hues of the printed wiring board. The inspection system performs at a 99.96% recognition rate and an average speed of

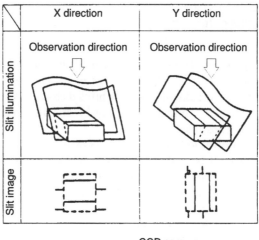

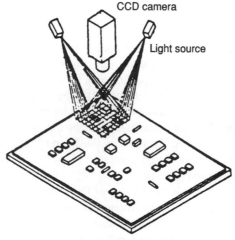

Fig. 2   Sectional lighting (1 of 2).

150 ms per component, including the substrate loading time. In addition to the above methods, devices using laser beam scanning or multiple cameras have also been developed.

SOLDER INSPECTION TECHNOLOGY

The automated inspection of solder conditions is very difficult but strong demand has led to brisk technological development over the past 2 to 3 years. The procedure consists of visual inspection to detect solder amount and solder bridges and

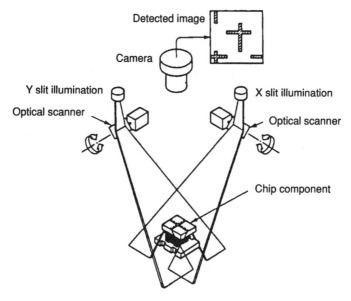

Fig. 3 Sectional lighting (2 of 2)

internal defect inspection to detect voids and cracks in the solder joint. Higher mounting density in recent years has prompted an increasingly stronger demand for internal defect inspection.

Functional Requirements of Automated Inspection

Table 2 lists the functions required of automated inspection. With actual results from the production line still scarce, some requirements are as yet unclear. A representative example of inspection items is shown, but the actual part types will cover a wide variety of items. Compared with the inspection of mounted components, a minimum of two points on each component are inspected, with an average of three to four points. Because of the large number of components being inspected, the inspection speed is a rigorous 10 to 20 ms per point.

TABLE 2   Functional Requirements for Solder Inspection

Items to be inspected	Rectangular chips, round chips, irregular-shaped chips, minimold transistors, SOP, QFP
Points of inspection	Presence of solder, amount of solder, bridges, voids, cracks
Reliability	Recognition rate of 99.98% or greater
Speed	10 to 20 ms per component

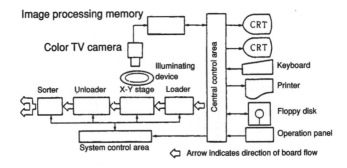

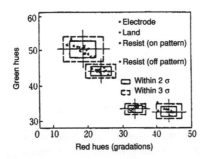

Fig. 4   System configuration and color separation of the printed wiring board.

Technological Issues

Technological issues involve 1) developing inspection methods, 2) achieving high-speed processing, and 3) quantifying judgment standards.

Inspection Methods. The condition of the solder's surface is reflective and is difficult for vision processing to discern. Because the solder joints of fine-pitch quad flat packages (QFPs) that have been reflowed are extremely thin and small, a high degree of accuracy is required. Some inspection items cannot be detected with two-dimensional inspection, making three-dimensional inspection a requirement. X-ray, ultrasonic wave, and infrared detection methods are used for internal defect inspection.

High-speed Processing. To achieve an inspection time of 10 to 20 ms/point, near real-time processing is needed. Techniques that can be used include pipeline processing and hard coding the instructions into the hardware.

Quantifying Judgment Standards. The soldering condition differs not only with the soldering method (i.e., whether flow or reflow) but also according to the type of component (rectangular chip, SOP, QFP), its size, and the amount of positional displacement. This makes quantifying judgment standards vital to supporting the inspection method.

Technological Trends in Visual Inspection

New types of visual inspection equipment have been introduced that determine acceptance or rejection based on reflective angle and quantity of laser light, or on sectional lighting.

Laser Method. This method vertically illuminates the sample with a helium–neon laser through a galvano-mirror [6]. The soldering condition is inspected by identifying the direction, strength, and temporal coordinates of the reflected light by a flat photosensor on the inner surface of the photosensor box. Photosensors are fixed on six surfaces: the four sides (A, B, C, and D), the top (E), and the sweep window (F). Figure 5 shows the inspection principles and an example of the laser beam sweep. Inspection of bridges, solder wetting condition, and lifted leads can be made with this method.

Three-Dimensional Shape Recognition. Three-dimensional inspection relies on the mirror-like condition of the solder surface and detects the local gradient angle of the solder surface based on the position of the light relative to the camera. The three-dimensional shape of the solder surface is derived from this gradient angle [7].

As Fig. 6 shows, multiple LEDs are arranged along the front of the solder surface. When these LEDs are lit in succession (changing the angle of illumination), a coalescence point (area of specular reflection) corresponding to each LED is generated. These coalescence points are captured by the camera. With this done, the position and inclination (X, Y, and q) of each coalescence point on the solder surface can be determined from the relationship between the LED's illumination angle and the capture angle. Next, the three-dimensional shape can be found by integrating the position and inclination of the coalescence points derived above.

Figure 7 is an example of the results from inspecting the solder surface on a QFP. Shown in Fig. 7a is the three-dimensional shape. Shown in Fig. 7b, c, and d are examples of cross-sectional shapes of joints with sufficient solder, no solder, and insufficient solder, respectively.

In addition to these two techniques, there are also methods for visual inspection that capture a reflected image by direct illumination (fluorescent lamp) and use the amount and direction of distortion to determine the solder condition. Another method uses color image processing.

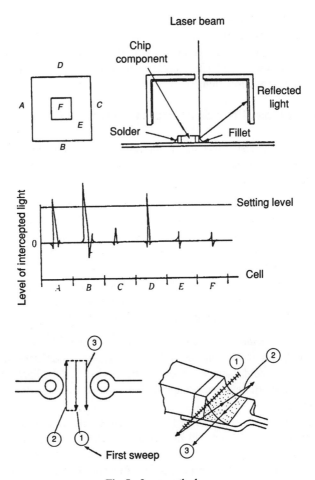

Fig. 5   Laser method.

Trends in the Inspection of Internal Defects

Internal defect inspection includes the inspection of voids and cracks as well as other conditions that cannot normally be inspected visually. This includes, for example, inspection of a QFJ's lead joint area or a QFP's lead heel area.

The development of practical equipment for inspecting internal defects has been limited because of problems such as the lack of a suitable inspection methodology, lengthy inspection times, and expensive equipment. Regardless, with companies beginning to use high density interconnection with QFJ, COB (chip on board), and COG (chip on glass) methods, inspection for internal defects is becoming indispensable for assuring product quality.

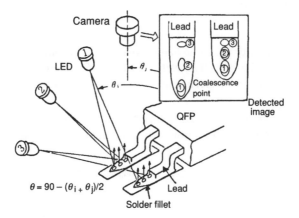

Fig. 6   Principle of three-dimensional inspection.

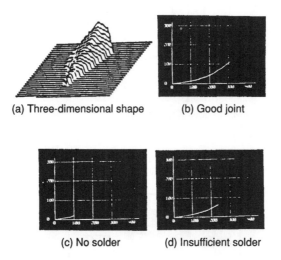

(a) Three-dimensional shape   (b) Good joint

(c) No solder   (d) Insufficient solder

Fig. 7   Detected shape (increment: μm).

The inspection methods announced to date include a system that heats the solder joint with a laser and analyzes the resulting infrared rays, one that vibrates the solder joint and determines the joint's condition displacement, and one that relies on x-rays.

X-Ray. Inspection equipment is being developed that uses x-ray images [8]. Until now, the x-ray method has been plagued by problems of low image contrast and poor resolution. However, a new microfocus-type x-ray source, which has a small focal point, makes this method much more practical. While its main use is to inspect for internal defects such as bridges and cracks, with the trend toward higher density its use is being expanded to encompass parts that cannot ordinarily be visually inspected, such as PLCCs, PGAs, and J-lead QFJs. Figure 8 shows the principles of inspection and an example of its use.

Temperature Change. The temperature change method inspects the solder joints by heating them with a laser beam and then capturing the change in tem-

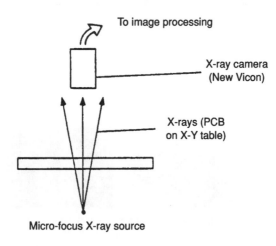

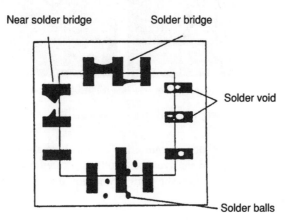

Fig. 8   X-ray inspection principle and an example.

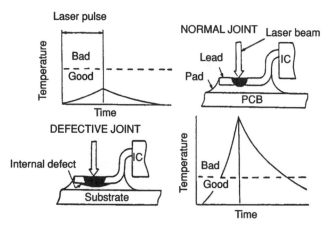

Fig. 9 Inspection by temperature change.

perature with an infrared camera [9]. Using a perfect solder joint as a reference, the method detects solder joints different from this reference and deems them to be defective. Internal defects such as voids and cracks, as well as the final condition of the solder joint, can be detected.

CONCLUSION

The use of automated inspection equipment on the manufacturing floor is being spurred by the inability of visual inspection to efficiently handle the increasing density of interconnection.

However, not all requirements for automating inspection are being met sufficiently. Although many problems remain with inspection techniques, in recent years PCB inspection technology has made notable advances with the development of a number of inspection methods.

The future of visual inspection will demand not only increased reliability of inspection, but also super high speed, high resolution, and general-purpose functionality. Practical equipment will be developed and continue to be introduced into manufacturing lines.

With regard to the inspection of internal package defects, expectations that so far have been vague will become concrete demands. The PGA and J-lead packages mentioned above are examples of this.

Furthermore, it is important that the equipment be able to quickly and easily register the enormous amount of inspection data. We anxiously await the development of intelligent systems with a learning capability.

REFERENCES

[1] Shiozaki, "Trends in testing and inspecting PCBs," *'88 JPCA Show: New Technology Seminar Text,* pp. 101–108, 1988.

[2] Uno et al., "PCB inspection equipment," *Toshiba Review,* vol. 42, no. 2, pp. 101–104, 1987.

[3] Kishimoto, et al., "Inspection equipment for fully automated chip mounting," *Sensor Technology,* vol. 7, no. 12, pp. 57–61, 1987.

[4] Inoue et al., "Inspection equipment for mounting irregular-shaped chips," *Toshiba Review,* vol. 43, no. 6, pp. 525–528, 1988.

[5] Takahara, "Automating visual inspection of surface mounted printed substrates," *Omron Techniques,* vol. 27, no. 4, pp. 364–372, 1987.

[6] Muraoka, "Visual inspection equipment for solder using laser beams," *Denshi Zairyo,* pp. 64–69, November 1988.

[7] Uno et al., "Solder inspection technology," *Proc 4th Printed Circuit Board Association Conference,* pp. 135–136, 1989.

[8] Miyata, "Interconnect quality inspection equipment," *Electronic Packaging Technology,* vol. 4, no. 12, pp. 61–64, 1988.

[9] R. Vanzetti, A.C. Traub, "Thermal energy as a diagnostic tool," *Sensors Journal,* vol. 2, no. 3, pp 17–29, March 1985.

Basics and Current State of Thermal Design

Wataru Nakayama

Tokyo Institute of Technology
Department of Engineering

INTRODUCTION

With the widespread use of surface mount technology, electronic equipment now demands precise thermal design. In other words, because integrated circuit (IC) packages are located closer together, a board's heat flux is higher. Moreover, differences in thermal expansion among the board, IC packages, and other parts cause repetitive stress to the solder bonds. The reliability of these bonds rests largely on the quality of thermal design. In response to these demands, a computer-aided design (CAD) program combining thermal design with reliability evaluation is available [1]. Aside from this, various documents have presented thermal design examples, making a fair amount of information relating to thermal design available today. However, it can be said that not many general purpose design methods exist that can be directly applied to the individual problems confronting the designer. In the future, it is also unlikely that any general purpose design methods will be established. Therefore, the best method continues to involve taking data obtained from many sources as a guide and coupling the data with an examination method that can be simply and easily carried out. This paper explains the basics of thermal design, its current state, and offers some simple methods of examination.

BASICS OF THERMAL DESIGN

Estimating Required Cool Air Volume

The first step in thermal design is to estimate the required cooling air volume (see Fig. 1). The required cooling air volume $\dot{V}$ (m³/s) is determined so that the air temperature at the exit of the body T_e (°C) does not exceed a limiting value. Namely, this is

$$T_e = T_1 + \frac{Q}{\rho C_p \dot{V}} < T_{e*} \tag{1}$$

where ρ (kg/m³) is the density of cooling air, C_p (J/kg·K) the specific heat at constant pressure, T_1 (°C) the air temperature at the cabinet entrance, and Q(W) the gross heat production. T_{e*} represents the limiting value of the air temperature at the body exit and is determined from the thermal equation. After the required cooling air volumetric flow rate is found, consideration must be given to whether natural cooling is possible or, in the case of forced cooling, to the selection of the fan.

As shown in Fig. 2, to do this it is necessary to know the cabinet or flow channel resistance curve with respect to the fan's characteristics and the buoyancy drive curve. Here, ΔP (Pa) indicates the pressure difference between the body's entrance and exit, and v (m/s) the air velocity. Taking A_c (m²) as the cross-sectional area of the passage and v as the flow velocity determined by matching the fan's properties and flow resistance, the air volume can be found from the equation $\dot{V} = v^* A_c$. A_c and v use the value found at a specific location within the body. An upper limit for v^* is determined by the ambient noise limit of the cool air. Therefore, when v^* exceeds this upper limit, changes to the passage design

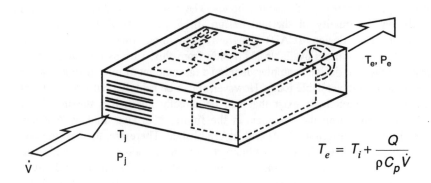

Fig. 1 Thermal design fundamental I: deriving the required local cooling load.

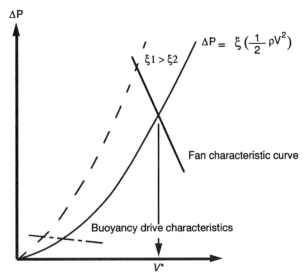

Fig. 2 Flow system resistance and cooling circulation drive force.

must be made. With natural cooling, even a slight increase in passage resistance reduces greatly the air flow velocity.

Estimating Thermal Resistance

A chip's heat dissipation value q (W) is comprised of q_{ca} (W), the component transmitted directly to the cooling air, and q_{ba}, the component directed to the air after being transmitted first to the board.

Figure 3 shows a double-sided assembly and the relatively large increase in the q_{ca} component that accompanies greater mount density. Figure 4 shows the circuit network of the thermal resistance about the package periphery. θ_J (°C) indicates junction temperature, θ_{jc} (°C/W) the thermal resistance between the junction and package surface, T_c (°C) the package surface temperature, θ_{ca} (°C/W) the package surface thermal resistance, θ_{cb} (°C/W) the path thermal resistance from the package to the board via the leads and solder paste, T_b (°C) the board temperature, θ_{ba} (°C/W) the board surface's thermal resistance, and T_a (°C) the cooling air temperature near the package.

Estimating the junction temperature and the board temperature is important for a surface mount board. In order to estimate thermal stress to the bonds between board and packages, both the board and package temperatures must be found. With through-hole boards in the past, thermal design often was simply done by using the combined thermal resistance θ_{ja} (°C/W) between the junction

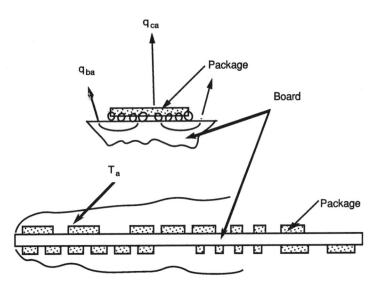

Fig. 3   Thermal design fundamental II: Deriving thermal resistance.

and air. In comparison, each component (θ_{jc}, θ_{ca}, θ_{cb}, and θ_{ba}) of thermal resistance must be known for surface mount boards.

T_{e*} of (1) is the maximum allowable value of T_a located near the cooling air exit and can be determined from the combined thermal resistance, value θ_{ja}, and the maximum allowable value T_{j*} of T_j (80–150°C but this value depends on the useful life specification).

CURRENT STATE OF THERMAL DESIGN

It is not easy to carry out thermal design as summarized above. The reasons for this and points that must be kept in mind during actual design follow.

Distribution of Rate of Air Flow within Cabinet

In order to derive thermal resistance, components θ_{ca} and θ_{ba} in Fig. 3, and the air velocity near the package must be known. But, the passage construction typically is complex, making it difficult to calculate the air flow rate's distribution ahead of time. This is because very little of the data related to the flow resistance coefficient x of Fig. 2 is actually useful.

To obtain data on local flow velocity and to prevent hot spots from occurring within the body, the inspection method shown in Fig. 5 works well. In the example in Fig. 5, the outer panel of the body is replaced with a clear acrylic

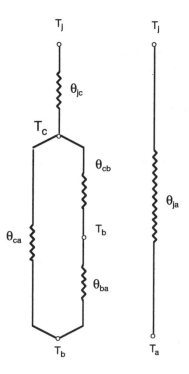

Fig. 4   Thermal resistance circuit.

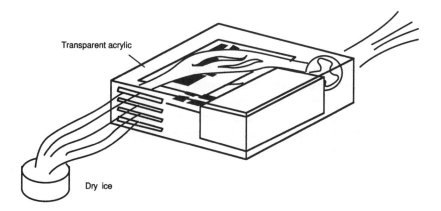

Fig. 5   Visualization of cooling current in the case.

panel, so the air flow within the body can be observed by using vapor given off by dry ice. With parameters that are easily changeable (such as the fan's arrangement, entrance grill arrangement, and filters) the resultant changes in the flow rate distribution can be observed.

Natural Convective Cooling

Estimating both the passage resistance and the fluid drive potential is difficult. One experimental estimation method has been announced that can be done relatively simply [2]. An infrared scanner is effective with current measures to observe the heat distribution of the board.

Thermal Resistance Values θ_{jc} and θ_{ja}

Thermal resistance θ_{jc} is the function of the encapsulant, lead frame material, structure, and dimensions, and so on. The properties of each component material are functions of the composition and can be seen in documents covering a wide range (see Table 1). The sealant's material properties strongly influence the type and density of the filler, especially with plastic packages. To give a measure of reference, a plastic package would be $\theta_{jc} = 10$ to $50°C/W$ [3], with θ_{jc} decreasing as the surface area increases. When the encapsulant is ceramic, θ_{jc} becomes one-half to one-fifth that of a plastic package of equal pin count [4]. To estimate θ_{jc} accurately, an understanding of material properties and a heat transfer analysis by numeric calculation are required.

Approximately 15 to $100°C/W$ surface thermal resistance is added to θ_{jc} when θ_{jc} is measured at the natural air cooled state [5]. When the package is placed on the board and force-cooled, the surface thermal resistance, which seems to include θ_{ca} and θ_{ba}, decreases by an order of several tens of °C/W from the value when naturally cooled, while θ_{ja} becomes 5 to $30°C/W$.

Data for θ_{jc} and θ_{ja} obtained from the package supplier can be used as a guide, but in many cases the test conditions are not disclosed. For precision thermal design, measurement under conditions resembling actual use is a must. Of particular importance are the measurements of θ_{ca} and θ_{ba}. For these, a heat transfer test is carried out by mounting dummy ceramic packages of like dimensions that have heaters built in.

Package Arrangement on Board

To increase reliability, it is typically advisable to place components generating high heat upstream of the cooling passages. While this may increase tem-

TABLE 1   Properties of Various Materials

	Heat Transfer Rate (W/m°C)	Thermal Expansion Rate (10^{-6}/°C)
Silicon	105–150 (100°C) – (30°C)	2.6–4.0
Aluminum	200	23–24
Copper	400	17
Alloy 42	15	5–9
Kovar	15	4.1–5.3
Alumina Ceramics	15–44	6–8
Glass-epoxy	0.16–1.6	13–46
Polyimide	0.35	12–16
Solder	35–50	21.5–24.7

peratures of other components slightly, the reliability of the entire system is improved.

Considerations in the Heat Design Approach

To tackle heat design head-on requires a fair amount of time and tools, such as test models and analysis programs. It is crucial that due consideration be given in advance to the degree of precision temperature estimates must meet and that cost benefits be ascertained. When doing so, the following factors should be examined.

- Consequences of product failures to society and safety
- Ease of producing the product
- Ease of real body tests and design changes (as a substitute method of detail design work)

For surface mount, a particularly important problem is stress to the solder joints caused by the repetitive temperature cycles incurred when powering the device on and off. When power is applied, the package's temperature rises rapidly, making the possibility high that larger thermal expansion differences will occur between the board and package. Thermal expansion is an important material property and thus must be fully considered. At the same time, it is important to carry out a suitable acceleration test to establish an accurate estimation of the product's life cycle.

After drawing up a rough thermal design, it is important to then focus closely on heat problems near packages with high heat generation. In other words, a system should be implemented that begins with determining the required cool air flow rate and then follows by estimating the body's capacity distribution. For the most critical areas, methods to increase the capacity should be examined and the air's local temperatures and local heat transfer rates estimated. Most problems stem from faulty systems rather than from imprecise heat calculations.

CONCLUSION

Progress in thermal design will come about with designers digesting and incorporating ever greater amounts of related information and accumulating experience. This writer is striving to make relative information generally available by organizing an electronic equipment cooling session for the Japan Society of Mechanical Engineers, presiding over workshops for the institute's heat engineering department, and organizing each of the various international societies. We ask that all readers participate actively. For a detailed survey of thermal design, please refer to [6].

REFERENCES

[1] Ohnishi et al., "Heat analysis system," *Electronics Mounting Technology*, vol. 4, no. 5, pp. 52–56, 1988.

[2] M. Ishizuka et al., "Air resistance coefficients for perforated plates in free convection," *ASME J. Heat Transfer*, vol. 109, pp. 540–543, 1987.

[3] S. W. Hinch, *Handbook of Surface Mount Technology*, Longman Scientific & Technical, 1988, pp. 69–72.

[4] Nakayama, "Cooling technology for electronic devices," *Journal of the Japan Mechanical Society*, vol. 88, no. 802, pp. 1048–1053, 1988.

[5] D. L. Waller et al., "Analysis of surface mount thermal and thermal stress performance," *IEEE Trans.*, vol. CHMT-6, no. 3, pp. 257–266, 1983.

[6] W. Nakayama, "Thermal management of electronic equipment: A review of technology and research topics," *Applied Mechanics Reviews* ASME, vol. 39, no. 12, pp. 1847–1868, 1986.

Index